Managing Conflict
Finding Meaning

Supporting Families at Life's End

Edited by Kenneth J. Doka and Amy S. Tucci

HOSPICE FOUNDATION
OF AMERICA

This book is part of Hospice Foundation of America's *Living with Grief*® series.

This book is part of HFA's *Living with Grief*® series.

Ordering information:

Call Hospice Foundation of America: 800-854-3402

Or write:
Hospice Foundation of America
1710 Rhode Island Avenue, NW #400
Washington, DC 20036

Or visit HFA's Web site:
www.hospicefoundation.org

Managing Editor: Lisa McGahey Veglahn
Layout and Design: HBP, Inc.

Publisher's Cataloging-in-Publication
(Provided by Quality Books, Inc.)

    Managing conflict, finding meaning : supporting families
      at life's end / edited by Kenneth J. Doka and Amy S. Tucci.
        pages cm. – (Living with grief series)
        Includes bibliographical references and index.
        LCCN 2015959038
        ISBN 978-1-893349-20-9

        1. Terminal care. 2. Families. 3. Conflict management.
    4. Bereavement—Psychological aspects.
    I. Doka, Kenneth J., editor. II. Tucci, Amy S., editor.
    III. Hospice Foundation of America. IV. Series: Living
    with grief.

R726.8.M27 2016   362.17'5
                      QBI15-600231

Dedication

To Lynn Vigliotti-Miller

*In appreciation
for over 50 years of friendship*

*And in admiration
of her ability to grow from grief*

KJD

Contents

Acknowledgments

We always begin by acknowledging our small staff of the Hospice Foundation of America, who work tirelessly to produce webinars and *Journeys: A Newsletter to Help in Bereavement*, as well as the annual Living with Grief® program and book.

We also thank a supportive Board of Directors for their ongoing efforts. Their counsel keeps us grounded and the Foundation running.

Special recognition goes to Managing Editor Lisa McGahey Veglahn, who carefully oversaw all aspects of this book. Lisa is more than a managing editor—she acts as our first critic—catching every error and clarifying each assumption.

Most importantly, we need to thank the authors who responded to tight deadlines, numerous queries, requests for revisions, and for dealing with the headaches that editors inevitably bring. We so appreciate how they have brought their theoretical expertise and clinical skills to each case chapter.

Both editors would like to thank their families and friends for their patience as we worked to publish a complex book in such a short time. You know who you are.

The Foundation exists through the assistance of our partners, sponsors, and many contributors. We are grateful for your help.

Introduction

Kenneth J. Doka

When I was younger, one of my favorite activities was caving or spelunking, exploring non-commercial caves. Caves are made, over eons, from water dissolving limestone. On one caving trip, I took my 11-year-old godson Scott. He happily sloshed through the cave with the rest of the club, sometimes crawling or slithering through particularly tight passages. At one point, the cave seemed to end in a small shallow pond. Yet the pond merely obscured a final passage. One had to go underwater, hand-in-hand with another explorer, squeezing through a narrow submerged passage before entering a final section to exit.

Scott was reluctant but after considering the option of returning to the opening where we had entered, he decided to proceed. After we made it through the passage, I remarked that it was brave of him to face his fears. He replied that his dad frequently said there were times he had to choose to grow up or grow down.

I regularly think of that comment. While not a completely literal translation, the Chinese word for *crisis* is often described as an amalgamation of the characters for *challenge* and *opportunity*. A crisis at the end of life offers both challenge and opportunity. We can grow up—or grow down.

The cases in this book illustrate challenges surrounding dying and grieving as well as opportunities that arise from crises. Names and some circumstances have been altered to protect privacy. The book begins with an excellent overview by Boelk and Kramer, highlighting some practical advice for professionals supporting families in conflict. The overview contains examples from nurses, social workers, and other professionals about how they've put that advice into practice.

The first section focuses on challenges. At a time of crisis, early conflicts can be exacerbated. Ribarich's case on addiction, and Stephenson and Grottanelli's case about a preexisting mental illness, illustrate the ways these problems can continue to complicate care at life's end. Cagle reminds us that pain management can also be a source of contention within families and between families and staff. Cagle reinforces the need for staff to educate and incorporate the family in pain management.

Other difficulties can be relatively new. For example, as Glajchen and Eisinger indicate, the challenges of caregiving can create or intensify family conflict, a point also underlined in Doka's chapter on disclosure, as well as in Schachter and Randhawa's case. These cases also show how the cultural context can generate conflict within the family and impair communication between family and staff. Meris' case also painfully demonstrates the multiple consequences that can occur when communication is stifled; in this instance, lack of communication caused conflict between a biological family and a gay man's partner, inevitably isolating the partner and exacerbating his grief.

Other aspects of context can also complicate care. Economic status can significantly impact access to care as well as quality of care. Financial constraints can limit caregiving options and even influence end-of-life decisions. Families who work full-time without a flexible schedule, or whose loved ones live in a different city, may find hospice care a challenge because no one in the family is available to provide home care between visits by hospice staff.

Two final chapters offer additional points. Harrington-LaMorie reminds us coping mechanisms that existed before the death can continue to cause conflict after the death. Doka's chapter emphasizes that medical staff can be deeply affected by the death of a patient; conflict may arise if medical staff disagree with the family's decisions at the end of life.

Collectively, these cases do not just delineate problems, they also suggest interventions. Improving communication within families and between families and medical staff is a critical component. Family meetings, as noted in a number of cases, may provide opportunities to do that. Other interventions, such as debriefings after difficult deaths and the use of rituals, may also be useful tools in resolving conflicts and enhancing communication. Yet, Meris' case offers a realistic and poignant caution: families can be complicated; not all problems can be resolved; not everyone lives happily ever after or even dies in peace with all issues resolved. Perhaps the test is not whether it was a "good death," however we define that, but rather if our interventions made the process a little better than it would have been.

We can also grow up, even at life's end. Montross-Thomas and Trejo's chapter emphasizes the growing body of evidence supporting Dignity Therapy, a very structured opportunity to empower life review. Perhaps, as the authors point out, one of the most important questions is: *When did you feel most alive?* This case reminds us that Dignity Therapy is not just about leaving a legacy but also recapturing a sense of life even as one is dying.

Doka explores a possible distinction between posttraumatic growth and resilience, noting a curvilinear relationship between these two concepts. Posttraumatic growth emerges out of struggle; while some resilience is necessary for growth, individuals with high levels of resilience adapt naturally to loss.

Stewart's case reinforces the notion that growth in grief is not limited to adults. Her case, exploring how three children in the same family respond to the death of their father, reminds us that children will respond differently, depending on their own developmental levels, and that interventions need to be tailored accordingly. Finally, she reiterates that even children are capable of growth as they grieve.

Moore's and Harpel's cases each describe situations of posttraumatic growth. Both offer strategies such as writing and journaling that can be employed by therapists seeking to assist growth. Doka briefly delineates many other ways that growth can be experienced. Harpel's case on suicide is complemented by Ruocco's personal narrative of how her family struggled, yet grew, as they coped with their father's death by suicide. In Neimeyer's case on perinatal loss, he offers a detailed account of the ways that a meaning-making strategy can facilitate growth. Gileno, too, emphasizes one person's search for meaning after loss. While Gileno describes a variety of therapeutic modalities, the use of support groups emerges as another way to facilitate growth. Doka's case on Rosa adds another intervention to the therapist's toolkit as he explores the ways that therapeutic ritual can foster growth. Finally, Shear, Skritskaya, and Gribbin show how Complicated Grief Therapy can foster growth, even in the most difficult circumstances.

Together, the chapters reaffirm that in a variety of circumstances, and with clients of all ages, growth is possible. More important, they offer the therapist a range of tools to facilitate that process of growth and finding meaning.

Overview

Professional Responses to Family Conflict at the End of Life

Amy Z. Boelk and Betty Kramer

Hospice and palliative care clinical and regulatory guidelines mandate attention to family functioning and the family context because responsiveness to the whole family is recognized as a component of optimal, quality hospice and palliative care services. Professionals report feeling ill-prepared to address family conflict in their work, though, often taking a hands-off approach when they do not see the conflict as amenable to change or within the parameters of their roles. While it may sometimes be appropriate not to respond to family conflict in keeping with family wishes and needs, preventative efforts may reduce the likelihood of conflict for all families, and careful responses may serve to ameliorate it for many.

Preventative efforts: Designed to prevent family conflict from occurring
- Upon intake, assess for history of conflict and other factors known to put families at risk of conflict at the end of life so that these concerns may be taken into consideration in determining the needs of the family and developing the care plan.
- Designate a family spokesperson to streamline communication among family and between family and providers, being careful to assure that the lines of communication between the identified spokesperson and other family members are open.
- Keep notebooks in the patient's home/room for family and providers to document visits, patient status, and patient needs, in an effort to avoid miscommunication.

- Provide proactive end-of-life education to multiple family members or through the family meeting(s) to enhance mutual understanding of diagnosis, disease progression, care strategies, and patient needs, particularly related to pain management and symptom control.
- Facilitate advance planning to clarify and document patient preferences and wishes, as well as engage family in preparing for future care needs.

Diffusing conflict: Designed to lessen or resolve existing family conflict

- Encourage family members to set conflict aside to focus on patient needs.
- Help family members problem-solve about how to directly address conflict.
- Provide supportive counseling to diffuse heightened emotions.
- Reframe family member behaviors to help family members "see the other side."
- Encourage family members to "share the care."

A Hospice Social Worker Reflects on her
Use of Reframing to Diffuse Conflict

His wife was the caregiver and he didn't want her taking care of him. He was still the man. They were bickering all the time as she was trying to take care of him. On one particular visit I made, he was nasty to her and she left the room crying. After she left, he said to me, "What's the big deal with her?" All I had to do was follow up on his lead by saying, "Well you know, she's really just trying so hard to take care of you out of love and I know it's difficult for you to accept that. You're very lucky to have her so that you can be here at home, where you want to be. Obviously, she feels very, very badly for what you said to her." During the next visit, his wife said to me, "I don't know what you said to him, but boy, he's a different person. He treats me so well now."

Aligning perceptions: Designed to help family members reach an agreement or mutual understanding regarding the patient's health status, care needs, and wishes

- Provide end-of-life education to multiple family members or through the family meeting(s) to get everyone "on the same page."
- Validate the patient's wishes to align the family with those wishes when they are discrepant.

A Hospice Nurse Reflects on her Use of Education
to Align Perceptions

One family member did not want to give the medication, thinking that it was going to make her mom too sleepy, but other family members wanted the medication given. I made a visit to explain to each family member the reasoning for the medication in an attempt to help them all understand. It came to the point where the family agreed that she needed the medication so that she was not restless. And they could see that she was just more comfortable. Giving information and education to the family can help them become more cohesive and work together.

Enhancing communication: Designed to address communication constraints that are fueling conflict

- Facilitate discussion of end-of-life issues and necessary decisions.
- Encourage or facilitate communication with distanced family members.

A Hospice Social Worker Reflects on her Efforts to Facilitate
Communication with a Distanced Family Member

We have gotten somewhere with the family by doing care conferences and inviting the daughter who lives out of town to be there by Skype to hear what's going on and see what's going on. It has allowed us to lay some groundwork for how we're going to communicate, and it has allowed her to witness us communicating things with her father, who is the caregiver. We also do a lot of emailing and make a lot of phone calls. Involving her more has reduced the tension in recent months.

Mitigating distress: Used when the conflict itself is not amenable to change

- Increase hospice support (respite, more visits, volunteers).
- Provide supportive counseling (listen, validate, allow to vent).
- Connect the family to resources outside of hospice, such as additional counseling services.
- Normalize family conflict.

A Hospice Nurse Reflects on the Use of Increased Visits and Supportive Counseling to Reduce Distress

The adult children, abused by the father in younger years, were dealing with these issues of, "I feel guilty because I wanted him to die and now he's dying." They'd feel strong one day and they'd want to be there and do everything they could, and then all of a sudden, the next day it would be like, "I don't want anything to do with this. I can't handle it anymore." We had social workers visit daily and maintain close contact with the family. We tried to have only a couple of nurses go in that the family could learn to trust because trust was an issue for them. We encouraged the use of spiritual services. We tried to do whatever we could to help them talk about how they were feeling and what they needed. We gave them as many opportunities as possible to express their feelings while showing a very nonjudgmental attitude. We tried to convey that "what your dad did was wrong but we're still going to care for him." We did a lot of "lifting them up" with acceptance for who they were.

Facilitating family meetings: A key approach to both prevent and respond to family conflict, fulfilling multiple aims simultaneously

- Unite and involve family members in the planning process.
- Ensure that family members receive the same education and information about the patient's health and needs.
- Open discussion about how communication will take place in the family and with healthcare providers.
- Allow opportunities to resolve existing disagreements.
- Promote trust between family members and healthcare providers.
- Provide opportunities for family members to share concerns, express needs, ask questions, and give input.

A Hospice Nurse Discusses the Utility of Family Meetings

If we feel like they're not communicating well or they have different understandings of things, the social worker will invite the family for a meeting. Family meetings help to get everybody in one place, hearing the same information at the same time and getting an opportunity to ask questions in front of each other. Usually, the first thing we do is allow them to ask questions so we hear what they want to know and what their goals are for the meeting. Then we just try to offer information and teaching so that everyone hears the same thing; then we can identify who is having trouble with accepting certain pieces of information. We try to make it relaxed and open so that people feel comfortable saying what's on their minds. It also helps to get everyone to agree on a plan - what do they want to do, how are they going to do it, who is going to do what? We put that right on the table so we can decide on a plan and how to proceed with that plan.

Adhering to a team approach: An important strategy to address family conflict and avoid professional fatigue

- Disperse responsibility among team members when working with families who have substantial needs due to conflict.
- Use expertise in various areas to best attend to family needs.
- Process conflict with team members in order to maintain objectivity.
- Maintain a united front and optimal communication among the team.

A Hospice Nurse Comments on the Value of a Team Approach

I use my team members because I may know the medical part of the situation, but I do not know the psychosocial piece; I do not know the spiritual; I do not know the grief. So, this is where I feel as though it's not what you know, it's who you know and how you get your concerns addressed. The hospice team working together with the family is very helpful in resolving conflict because each member can use their expertise in their specific field.

A Hospice Social Worker Comments on the
Need for a Team Approach

Sometimes the challenge for us in working with families in conflict is to have the team stay focused and objective. Now that we have partnered with nurses for our visits, it makes a really big difference. It helps in that you don't have one person feeling so entrenched in that family that it's hard to maintain objectivity.

This information was generated through a study involving focus groups with 37 hospice professionals including social workers, chaplains, bereavement coordinators, volunteer coordinators, nurses, and nursing assistants.

Amy Z. Boelk, PhD, MSSW, *is a professor in the Department of Sociology & Social Work at the University of Wisconsin–Stevens Point, where she also directs their BSW Program. A former hospice social worker, Dr. Boelk's research agenda has focused on various aspects of end-of-life care, including family conflict at the end of life, hospice care in rural communities, and recovery from parental suicide. Her research on family conflict at the end of life has been published and presented widely, with the aim of helping professionals in a variety of disciplines to better understand and respond to it. Dr. Boelk received her MSSW from the University of Wisconsin–Madison, and her PhD in social work from the University of Texas at Austin.*

Betty Kramer, PhD, MSSW, *is a professor in the School of Social Work at the University of Wisconsin–Madison where she also directs the part-time MSW program, and is a member of the Comprehensive Cancer Center. With her colleagues, Dr. Kramer established competencies and a national research agenda for social work research in palliative and end-of-life care and has been involved in several projects relevant to improving care of the dying. In addition to research on family conflict at the end-of-life, Dr. Kramer has focused on various aspects of caregiving and innovations in care for frail, low-income elders with advanced chronic disease. Dr. Kramer earned her MSSW from the University of Louisville and her PhD in social welfare from the University of Washington.*

Managing Conflict

CHAPTER 1

Susan's Story: Triumph Over Addiction at the End of Life

Marie Ribarich

CASE DESCRIPTION

Susan is a 50-year-old woman, a wife, mother of three, and grandmother of two. She lives in an affluent town in the suburbs of New York City. From all outward appearances, Susan has the perfect life: a devoted husband, successful children, a nice home, and a job that she loves. However, looks can be deceiving. One year ago, Susan experienced unusual back pain and went to her doctor for a check-up. The results of her physical revealed a spot on her liver that was confirmed to be a progressive form of cancer. Initial chemotherapy and radiation treatments seemed promising but last month, after complaining about increasing pain, she was told that the cancer had spread to other organs and had metastasized to her bones. Pain had become an even greater issue. Her doctor wanted to prescribe opioids for the bone pain, not knowing of Susan's history. Susan is a recovering addict whose drug of choice was Vicodin, a prescription opioid. Susan has not touched painkillers, not even non-narcotic NSAIDs or an aspirin, for five years. She had to tell her doctor the truth.

STATEMENT OF PROBLEM

Once Susan revealed her history of opioid addiction, she and her doctor were faced with the difficult task of pain management for her cancer. Susan's years of addiction had led to great strife in her marriage, the neglect of her children, bankruptcy, and a DUI charge. She did not want to return to the life of an addict, yet her pain was increasing and needed to be addressed. Susan's fears were twofold: that she would relapse even under the most controlled pain medication administration, and the quality of her remaining life would be compromised if the pain was not sufficiently managed.

ANALYSIS

Susan was a strong woman who had maintained her abstinence from prescription pain killers for five years. She knew too well from her history how medicating pain can lead to an addiction. Following a car accident 10 years ago, Susan had been prescribed Vicodin for neck pain. Even after there was no longer any physical indication for the prescription opioid, Susan had continued to use it in increasing doses until her drug use was out of her control. Now faced with a progressive, painful cancer, she had to summon up great strength to work with her doctor to manage her pain successfully and without consequence this time.

Prater, Zylstra, and Miller (2002) believe that, in dealing with pain management at the end of life, addiction should not be an issue. Comfort is the key factor regardless of a patient's addiction history. What needs to be addressed, they say, is the mechanism for pain management. According to Sean Mackey, Chief of Pain Management at Stanford University, there are several options for treating pain in opioid-dependent individuals (Vimont, 2011). Some of these include non-opioid medications including antiepileptic drugs, antidepressant drugs, NSAIDs, and psychological therapies. Mackey says that collaboration with all care providers is the key to success (Vimont, 2011). In Susan's case, her doctor believed that only an opioid painkiller would be successful against the kind of pain she was experiencing. This option plus psychotherapy was prescribed.

In order for Susan's pain management to be successful, the amount of opioids administered needed to be carefully monitored in order to avoid tolerance and relapse. However, as Susan began treatment, it became evident that she did indeed need greater doses. A determination had to be made if this was due to the progression of the cancer and its pain or to a relapse in her addiction. At this point, her counselor, who was an experienced addiction specialist, became a vital part of her treatment team.

GOALS OF COUNSELING

The initial goal of counseling was to address the heightened stress that Susan was experiencing because of her pain and the prescribed pain management plan. Individual therapy sessions were immediately begun to discuss her fears and concerns and to monitor and address any signs of relapse, either in her thinking or her behavior. Concurrent with the goal of avoiding relapse, counseling aimed to address unresolved emotions, fears, and issues regarding her cancer and the prospect of dying.

INTERVENTION STRATEGIES

As Susan began requiring greater doses of the pain medication, discussions focused on her perception of pain and on whether she was experiencing any euphoric effects of the medication. The therapist introduced stress management techniques that Susan could practice outside the session. She also encouraged Susan's return to 12-step meetings, which would provide greater social supports and fellowship with other recovering addicts during this challenging time. Counseling sessions with her husband and her family were conducted so that they could learn about Susan's physical condition and her addiction, and how to support her.

Susan spoke with her counselor often and regularly about not wanting to relapse, seeing her fight for recovery five years ago as the greatest achievement of her life. Now that she had won the battle over addiction she did not wish to return to that battlefield again; she wanted to direct all her strength to fight the cancer. Once pain management was begun, Susan was open and honest about the experience in therapy, attended local 12-step meetings twice a week, and embraced stress management and other alternative treatments such as acupuncture and yoga. Thoughts of getting high did indeed surface but she was able to work through them with the strength of her support system. She and the therapist also set up a series of reinforcements for appropriate pain medication use. At the end of every week, Susan would treat herself to her favorite dessert or to shopping if she followed the pain protocol without faltering. These activities seemed to be additional motivators.

As Susan continued in counseling, she began to reveal how she had been avoiding her feelings about the cancer, and she recognized this to be an old habit that had played a big role in her life of addiction. Although frightened and depressed, she knew she had to face her reality and that she needed the support of her husband and family to do so. Couples and family therapy provided an opportunity for the expression of feelings and unresolved issues of all family members. The goal was to encourage family healing, improve family functioning, and provide support to each member.

Conclusions and Reflections

Susan continued her fight with cancer for another six months before she died. During those six months, as the physical and emotional pain increased, Susan told her therapist she had many thoughts of escaping into drug use. This situation would not have been unusual, especially given her condition; the National Institute on Drug Abuse (NIDA) reports that the drug addiction relapse rate is 40% to 60% (NIDA, 2014). That overall rate is for all individuals, not those facing the additional challenges that Susan did. She could easily have rationalized her reasons for returning to the drugs in order to face her impending death. But in the end she did not relapse. She followed the pain protocol and adhered to the opioid contract she made with her doctor. She credited this success to her amazing collaborative support team of caregivers: doctors, therapists, family and friends, all of whom were quite astonished by her motivation, persistence, and strength of character.

Marie Ribarich, PhD, is an assistant professor of psychology and counseling in the Graduate School at The College of New Rochelle where she teaches Master's level courses in addictions, psychopathology, and counseling. Prior to her tenure at the College, Dr. Ribarich's professional experience included several years in the field of addiction treatment, including 10 years as the psychologist and coordinator of a women's and children's day treatment program. Licensed in New York State as a clinical psychologist, Dr. Ribarich's private practice focuses on the treatment of various issues affecting children, adolescents, adults, and families. Dr. Ribarich received her baccalaureate degree in psychology from New York University and her doctorate in clinical psychology from St. John's University in New York. In 2013, she completed a year-long post-graduate certificate program in Eating Disorders, Compulsions, and Addictions at the William Alanson White Institute in New York City.

REFERENCES

National Institute on Drug Abuse. (2014). *Drugs, brains, and behavior: The science of addiction.* Retrieved from https://www.drugabuse.gov/publications/drugs-brains-behavior-science-addiction/treatment-recovery

Prater, C. D., Zylstra, R. G., & Miller, K. E. (2002). Successful pain management for the recovering addict. *Primary Care Companion to the Journal of Clinical Psychiatry, 4*(4), 125-131.

Vimont, C. (2011) Challenges of treating chronic pain in people with opioid dependence. Retrieved from http://www.drugfree.org/join-together/addiction/challenges-of-treating-chronic-pain-in-people-with-opioid-dependence

CHAPTER 2

The Management of Patient Pain as a Potential Source of Family Conflict

John G. Cagle

Pain management can be a common source of tension for families caring for a hospice patient. Because hospice care typically is provided in a private residence, the responsibility for managing medication routinely falls upon a family caregiver with no medical training who often feels unprepared and uneasy when dealing with narcotic drugs or multiple, potentially interactive, medications. Keeping track of medications and monitoring adherence to a prescription regimen can be challenging for patients and caregivers and become additional sources of consternation. Given the inherent complexity of assessing and managing symptoms at the end of life, while also dealing with differing opinions and emotions about goals of care and optimal treatments, the potential for conflict is rife. Furthermore, when new pain treatments are started, family members and patients frequently have concerns about addiction, tolerance, stigma (i.e., being perceived as a drug seeker), side effects, or being a burden on others. These beliefs, which often are unwarranted, can stoke interpersonal conflict and hinder pain management efforts. Fortunately, addressing these common barriers to pain management with targeted, evidence-supported education can improve patient comfort, as well as caregiver knowledge and attitudes (Cagle et al., 2015).

Whether receiving hospice at home or in a long-term care setting, pain management can be a catalyst for heated disagreements. Family members may have strong opinions about the best way to treat patient discomfort. Some may question the use of narcotics, while others may question the use of non-pharmaceutical alternatives.

Family members also may be concerned about giving the patient too much pain medication (e.g., worries about overdose), or they may be worried about not giving enough. Disagreements also can arise when a patient is non-communicative and family members have differing interpretations of whether nonverbal cues are indicators of pain. These disagreements can be especially troubling when families push for treatments that conflict with what the patient would want (whether the patient's preferences are perceived by the family member or clearly documented in a written advance directive).

Conflict around pain management can continue even after the patient dies. Because higher doses of pain medication often are required to assuage discomfort as an illness progresses, some family members may attribute the patient's death to the medication, rather than the disease. This belief may manifest as caregiver guilt/self-blame; family members who were less involved in care may make unwarranted accusations that the patient was overdosed. Alternately, if the patient's pain was not able to be adequately controlled, family members may feel frustrated, helpless, or angry. When this happens, strong feelings and criticism, whether justified or not, may be directed at care providers.

It also is important to acknowledge some of the known health disparities in pain management at the end of life, as well as how cultural and familial norms can impact communication, responses to illness, and interactions with health providers. African American patients and families may treat hospice and palliative care providers with suspicion, as a legacy of cultural mistrust often complicates the establishment of family-provider rapport. Furthermore, racial and ethnic minority patients are more likely to experience undertreated pain at the end of life, adding a source for potential conflict (Anderson, Green, & Payne, 2009). Within each family context, cultural and familial norms will inform whether open disagreements about medical treatment are considered acceptable or rude. For example, some cultures place high value on agreement and consensus, while viewing dissent as impolite or disruptive. An in-depth assessment of family dynamics and valued cultural traditions may help providers navigate conflict, whether overtly displayed or hidden and communicated indirectly.

To avoid unnecessary conflict, facilitate communication among everyone involved in the patient's care, and optimize pain control, health providers can do the following:

- Document patient preferences for treatment and advocate for those preferences when patients cannot speak for themselves.
- Take a proactive approach to address the many myths and misperceptions about pain medication (e.g., concerns about addiction, side effects, tolerance).
- Educate families about the expected disease trajectory, including the potential need for opioid medication, and, if prescribed, how to dose and administer treatments.
- Ensure that all of the key stakeholders are included in the conversation when providing education and facilitating decisions with a family, particularly if multiple family caregivers are involved or expected to be involved.
- Normalize the experience; approximately 90% of hospice patients take some type of medication for pain.
- Screen both the patient and family caregiver(s) for a history of substance abuse; if positive, create a medication tracking plan that does not impede pain management, yet promotes accountability.
- Encourage open communication. Provide an opportunity for family members to ask questions and share concerns about treatments.
- Assess family dynamics and relevant beliefs about communication and pain management.

John G. Cagle, PhD, MSW, is an assistant professor at the University of Maryland School of Social Work in Baltimore, MD. His work focuses on the psychosocial dimensions of pain and pain management, particularly as they relate to care at the end of life. As a clinician-researcher, his scholarship is informed by nearly a decade of experience as a hospice social worker. His research has included clinical trials to assess for and address barriers to pain management in hospice care, efforts to improve palliative care in long-term care settings, and an evaluation of public perceptions about pain and pain medicines. His work has been supported by the John A. Hartford Foundation, the National Palliative Care Research Center, the Agency for Healthcare Research and Quality, and the National Institutes of Health.

References

Cagle, J. G., Zimmerman, S., Cohen, L., Porter, L., Hanson, L. & Reed, D. (2015). EMPOWER: An intervention to address barriers to pain management in hospice. *Journal of Pain and Symptom Management, 49*, 1-12. doi: 10.1016/j.jpainsymman.2014.05.007

Anderson K. O., Green, C. R., & Payne, R. (2009). Racial and ethnic disparities in pain: Causes and consequences of unequal care. *Journal of Pain, 10*, 1187-1204.

CHAPTER 3

Caring for a Patient with Schizophrenia at the End of Life

Pam Shockey Stephenson and Nan Grottanelli

Persons diagnosed with serious, persistent mental illnesses (SPMIs) can be challenging in any healthcare setting. However, situations where persons with SPMI also have a life-limiting illness create unique needs which are poorly understood (Baker, 2005; Madrigal, 2010). Several barriers interfere with patient care, including the (a) stigma of mental illness, (b) marginalization of persons with SPMI living in situations that make it unlikely they will access health care (e.g., homelessness, family estrangement, etc.), (c) suboptimal therapeutic relationships with healthcare professionals, and (d) lack of a strong research base about the needs of persons with SPMI and terminal illness (Madrigal, 2010; McCasland, 2007; Piatt, Munetz, & Ritter, 2010). This discussion will present the case of an older woman with a long history of schizophrenia who is also dying from end-stage chronic obstructive pulmonary disease (COPD).

CASE DESCRIPTION

JT is a 72-year-old black female with a long history of paranoid schizophrenia. JT has been living in a long-term care facility for three months but has recently been admitted to the hospice service with end-stage COPD. Co-morbid diagnoses include protein calorie malnutrition, morbid obesity, diastolic congestive heart failure, diabetes mellitus type 2, hyperlipidemia and peripheral neuropathy due to diabetes, essential hypertension, gout, chronic respiratory failure, and oxygen dependence.

A recent physical exam showed JT's vital signs to be within normal limits other than for rapid and labored respirations of 22/minute. Her oxygen saturation was 88% on 2 liters per nasal cannula. She is 5 foot 6 inches tall and weighs 486 pounds. Further physical examination was essentially unremarkable. JT was on numerous medications, which until recently included aripiprazole (Abilify), an atypical antipsychotic. JT began experiencing hand tremors from aripiprazole so her antipsychotic was changed to olanzapine (Zyprexa). This case study will examine issues directly related to this medication transition and discuss an overall plan of care for patients with life-limiting illness who also have a history of schizophrenia.

STATEMENT OF PROBLEM

Patients like JT with a dual diagnosis of SPMI and life-limiting illness require all of the services that hospice has to offer while managing the day-to-day challenges of their SPMI. Changing antipsychotic medications is one example of such a challenge that can contribute to the instability of psychiatric symptoms and, therefore, affect the physiological status of the patient. Decisions must be made by the healthcare team as to how quickly to change drugs, the necessity for changing drugs in light of a progressing illness, and the method of change to be utilized to minimize complications. This case exemplar will discuss the complexities of JT's care.

ANALYSIS

Analysis of the patient's current situation revealed two issues that were interfering with her care. First, she had been experiencing hand tremors for two weeks which was most likely from taking aripiprazole and was, therefore, changed to olanzapine to control paranoid schizophrenia. While the medication was being converted, the patient began exhibiting paranoid behaviors and accused the staff of giving her poison and killing her children. This led to the second issue interfering with JT's care; she became noncompliant with all medications and oxygen therapy and exhibited frequent outbursts that were both vocal and combative. The staff tried to reason with JT and explain why she needed the medications but JT screamed back, accusing them of trying to poison her. The staff felt unprepared to deal with JT's outbursts and while a few became frustrated and tried to coerce the patient into taking her medications, others were frightened and avoided interacting with JT.

GOALS OF COUNSELING

The way that patients with SPMI prepare for death is similar to those without SPMI except for the presence of additional symptoms from the SPMI that require management. The patient should receive counseling support from a mental health professional who has expertise in caring for schizophrenic patients. This is particularly important while JT is in crisis, during which time the goal is for JT to be compliant with her medications and reach therapeutic blood levels (Terpstra & Terpstra, 2012). Once JT's symptoms are better managed, she will benefit from additional counseling about dying from the hospice team. Counseling professionals would recognize the need to form a trusting relationship with JT that conveys respect and compassion (Baker, 2005). It is vital that JT have a safe place to talk about her disease symptoms and feelings about dying. Counselors could help JT with life closure by helping her prepare for death. Strategies for life review such as Dignity Therapy can be helpful because patients are guided through the exploration of their life's meaning to achieve closure (Chochinov et al., 2011). Counseling professionals should support staff with ongoing evaluation for medication toxicities as JT's organs continue to fail. This type of collaborative approach offers the best chance of noticing early changes in JT's condition, minimizing her risk of future crises, and enhancing the environment as JT nears the end of her life (Grottanelli & Stephenson, 2015).

INTERVENTION STRATEGY

Interdisciplinary care

The best approach to patient care with this population is interdisciplinary and includes experts from long-term, hospice, and psychiatric care. This approach allows all dimensions of the person (physical, social, psychological, and spiritual) and aspects of his or her care to be coordinated and addressed routinely. Furthermore, once JT is out of crisis, she should be included as part of the decision-making team as warranted and to the extent she is able (Terpstra & Terpstra, 2012). JT is legally competent and able to make her own medical decisions; however, other patients may be deemed incompetent and have a guardian appointed for medical decisions. All patients, however, should participate in decisions about their daily routines (e.g., the timing of morning hygiene). This involvement helps to restore the humanity of their situation, conveys a respectful and caring attitude from the staff, and builds trust. The need for building trusting relationships for patients with paranoid schizophrenia cannot be overstated (Baker, 2005).

Nursing care

It is common for nurses not usually caring for this population to feel some degree of discomfort. Whether it is because they do not understand the psychiatric condition, do not feel competent to make care-related decisions, are unable to effectively communicate with patients, or fear for their own safety from patient outbursts, each member of the nursing staff must recognize his or her degree of discomfort, determine if it will interfere with the ability to provide care, and initiate measures to reduce barriers. Not doing so increases the risk that staff will employ avoidance strategies with the patient, which will compromise patient care. Furthermore, patients may sense a staff member's discomfort, undermining the formation of a therapeutic relationship. Specific strategies of assuring patient safety and enhancing communication can improve care (Baker, 2005; Grottanelli & Stephenson, 2015; Terpstra & Terpstra, 2012).

Patient safety

Patients with schizophrenia in crisis are at a greater risk of injury from poor decision making and self-harm. Nursing staff must monitor the patient's environment frequently to assure that there is not access to dangerous objects or situations. Objects such as cords, bed linens, shower curtains, stainless-steel cutlery, electronics, and razors must be removed from the patient's room while at a high risk of self-injury. Patients with the greatest risk of injury might require one-on-one supervision, particularly if their call light is removed from the room because the cord poses a danger (Robinson, Littrell, & Littrell, 1999).

Minimizing the risk for violent outbursts and promoting patient comfort can be facilitated by ensuring that their exposure to stimuli is minimal. This includes dimming the lights in the patient's room and reducing noises in the hallway. Because patients requiring close supervision are often housed close to the nurses' station there is a greater tendency for noise. Closing the patient's door will interfere with the ability of maintaining close supervision of the patient and should not be used as a method of noise reduction. The nursing staff should continuously monitor for loud laughter or talking at the nurses' station or outside of the patient's room. Signage can be used to designate the hallway and nurses' stations as "quiet zones" but the staff will also need to be diligent and compliant. Keep in mind, however, that persons with paranoid schizophrenia might perceive whispering as being about them, which could also produce agitation. Patients respond best to calm environments that are predictable and organized. Familiarity and consistency with staff and patient schedules are also helpful (Grottanelli & Stephenson, 2015; Robinson et al., 1999).

In the event that a patient does become overly agitated, early intervention is key. A trusted member of the nursing staff can try to talk to the patient in a soothing manner before medications are employed, but staff members should never place themselves in danger if the patient is excessively violent or aggressive. Physical restraint is acceptable during a violent outburst if the patient is a danger to him/herself or others, but staff should follow their institution's policy for restraint and be certain that enough staff is available to restrain the patient safely.

Communication

Communication can be enhanced in several ways. Patients should be approached in a calm manner and spoken to clearly. Patients reporting delusions/hallucinations (D/H) should be reassured that although their D/H are real to them, the nurse does not see or hear what they do. Do not personify the voices a patient reports as this validates that the entities provoking the hallucinations are real. Instead, refer to them as "the voices" and not as "they." Patients experiencing suspicious paranoia should be approached in a manner that is assertive, matter-of-fact, and neutral. Do not touch patients if they do not expect it or consent. Cultural competence dictates that permission before touching should be practiced with all patients (D'Avanzo, 2008). This is no different for patients with SPMI. Explain any physical examinations or interventions that require touch before proceeding (Grottanelli & Stephenson, 2015; Walker, 2015).

CONCLUSIONS AND REFLECTIONS

Collaboration is the most important element when caring for patients with complex medical, emotional, social, and spiritual needs. Reaching out to additional experts for advice and collaboration will reduce staff frustrations, make the most efficient use of everyone's time, and ensure that the best care is provided which is ultimately reassuring to patients' families. JT was able to find shelter in a long-term care facility but many are not as fortunate. Family estrangement is common for many persons living with SPMI and the period of impending death for one family member can elicit guilt and shame from others. Staff need to acknowledge the situation and provide an empathetic environment for sharing a wide variety of emotions (Chochinov & Breitbart, 2009). Palliative and hospice care are meant to be equally available to everyone and a tremendous need exists in most communities to reach those with SPMI wherever they reside. This might include shelters or highway underpasses as many of these individuals are homeless (Baker, 2005; Madrigal, 2010). As we continue to learn more about patients with SPMI and terminal illness and adapt to caring for them wherever they live, palliative care will advance as a just and compassionate option for all persons with life-limiting illness.

Pam Shockey Stephenson, PhD, RN, AOCNS, PMHCNS-BC, is assistant professor at Kent State University's College of Nursing. Dr. Stephenson has clinical experience in medical and radiation oncology nursing and is credentialed as an Advanced Oncology and Psychiatric Mental Health Clinical Nurse Specialist. Her current program of research relates to how families transition towards the end of life when one parent has a life-limiting illness. In particular, Dr. Stephenson is working to develop a new construct for palliative care of spiritual uncertainty.

Nan Grottanelli, MSN, AGPCNP-BC, CHPN, is a nurse practitioner with Caremore in Richmond, Virginia. She presently is certified as a nurse in hospice and palliative care, and board certified as an Adult Geriatric Primary Care Nurse Practitioner. She is working with geriatric and geriatric psych patients in a wide variety of settings. Ms. Grottanelli has more than 40 years experience in health care in a wide variety of areas including geriatrics, psychiatry, hospice and palliative care, emergency, critical care, administration, education, alternative medicine, and malpractice. She is a national speaker and author.

REFERENCES

Baker, A. (2005). Point of view: Palliative and end-of-life care in the serious and persistently mentally ill population. *Journal of the American Psychiatric Nurses Association, 11*(5), 298-303.

Chochinov, H. M. & Breitbart, W. (2009). *Handbook of psychiatry in palliative medicine.* New York, NY: Oxford University Press.

Chochinov, H. M., Kristianson, I. J., Breitbart, W., McClement, S., Hack, T. F., Hassard, T., & Harlos, M. (2011). Effect of dignity therapy on distress and end-of-life experience in terminally ill patients: A randomised controlled trial. *Lancet Oncology, 12*(8), 753-762.

D'Avanzo, C. E. (2008). *Mosby's pocket guide to cultural health assessment* (4th ed.). Philadelphia, PA: Mosby Elsevier.

Grottanelli, N., & Stephenson, P. (2015). Psychiatric/psychological symptoms and diagnoses. In H. Martinez & P. Berry (Eds.), *Core curriculum for the hospice and palliative registered nurse* (4th ed.), (pp. 179-210). Dubuque, IL: Kendall-Hunt Publishing.

Madrigal, M. (2010). Understanding end-of-life care in schizophrenia: Mortality, stigma, and innovations. Retrieved from http://www.ehinstitute.org/articles.html

McCasland, L. A. (2007). Providing hospice and palliative care to the seriously and persistently mentally ill. *Journal of Hospice & Palliative Nursing, 9*(6), 305-315.

Piatt, E. E., Munetz, M. R., & Ritter, C. (2010). An examination of premature mortality among decedents with serious mental illness and those in the general population. *Psychiatric Services, 61*(7), 663-668. doi:10.1176/appi.ps.61.7.663

Robinson, L., Littrell, S. H., & Littrell, K. (1999). Managing aggression in schizophrenia. *Journal of the American Psychiatric Nurses Association, 5*(2), S9-16.

Terpstra, T. L. & Terpstra, T. L. (2012). Hospice and palliative care for terminally ill individuals with serious and persistent mental illness: Widening the horizons. *Journal of Psychosocial Nursing & Mental Health Services, 50*(9), 28-34. doi:10.3928/02793695-20120807-02

Walker, C. A. (2015). Caring for the patient with acute psychosis. *Nursing made incredibly easy, 13*(3), 40-47. doi:10.1097/01. NME.0000462645.52688.23

CHAPTER 4

Family Conflicts in Caregiving and Treatment

Myra Glajchen and Maj Eisinger

CASE DESCRIPTION

Ms. B is a 68-year-old woman with Stage IV gastric cancer metastatic to the liver. During treatment with epirubicin, cisplatin, and 5-FU, her disease progressed and she developed a painful polyneuropathy. A second therapy was tried, but she developed severe vomiting and further treatment was withheld. She was admitted to the hospital and symptoms improved with hydration and antiemetics.

Ms. B's oncologist offered her a Phase I clinical trial involving a new targeted chemotherapy. Although there was no strong clinical evidence of efficacy, he was optimistic because it was similar to other well-tolerated drugs which conferred a survival advantage of two to three months. While awaiting transfer to a subacute rehabilitation unit, Ms. B requested time to consider the options. She was fatigued with constant, severe, burning neuropathic pain in her feet and fingers. The pain worsened with activity, leaving her confined to bed or chair. Her fine motor movements became clumsy and she needed help with bathing and toileting. Anorexia was an increasing problem with a drop in her weight from 180 to 80 pounds.

After transfer to the rehabilitation unit, Ms. B began limited physical therapy and was referred to the palliative care consultation service for help with symptom control and discharge planning. The pain improved with a fentanyl patch, morphine for breakthrough pain, pregabalin, and nortriptyline, but her functional capacity remained poor.

STATEMENT OF PROBLEM

Ms. B has rapidly progressive gastric cancer despite first-line chemotherapy. An experimental Phase I trial drug has been offered to her, with unknown efficacy and unpredictable side effects. Ms. B is increasingly debilitated by anorexia, weight loss, cachexia, fatigue, unrelenting pain, depression and anxiety.

Through a comprehensive psychosocial assessment, the palliative social worker learns that Ms. B is a widow and matriarch of a large, close-knit family. Although she lives alone, three children live nearby and visit regularly. The oldest daughter, who lives in a different state, is the designated healthcare agent. Ms. B has a close relationship with her sisters; they worship at the same church. Two years ago, a fourth sister died after being diagnosed with cancer; she opted for a holistic medical approach.

The social worker becomes aware of divisive undercurrents of family opinion. This family has watched one sister die of metastatic cancer after declining conventional chemotherapy. The surviving sisters believe it was God's will that their sister died, and that the outcome of Ms. B's disease is also God's will. The children believe that their aunt "died too soon" and believe that Ms. B should accept the experimental chemotherapy. Ms. B's sisters believe that her children are unaware of the gravity of Ms. B's illness or the extent of her suffering. As the sisters are doing most of the caregiving, they also feel that they are in a better position to make decisions for Ms. B should the need arise.

In arranging a family meeting, the palliative social worker realizes there is disagreement between the oncologist and palliative care physician. In private, the oncologist gives Ms. B a life expectancy of three to six months, noting her increasing frailty. However, the oncologist prefers to maintain hope by offering new therapies and avoiding prognostication in discussions with Ms. B and her family. The palliative physician, while respecting the relationship between Ms. B and her oncologist, believes Ms. B cannot make appropriate decisions without realistic information. In fact, the palliative team has told Ms. B she is an ideal candidate for hospice.

ANALYSIS

This case highlights several important issues, including the impact of cultural and generational conflict within families, managing conflict among treating teams, and honoring the patient's voice in decision making. The younger members of the family believe in the power of the experimental chemotherapy; Ms. B's sisters have faith in the divine and favor a more "natural" approach. The oncologist and the palliative care team are not in agreement with each other and have presented options that are in conflict. There is dissension about the role of the oldest daughter as a healthcare agent, although Ms. B designated her; in fact, the patient's voice has been muted by divisive family opinions.

GOALS OF COUNSELING

The palliative care team suggests a family meeting to discuss the clinical trial and Ms. B's needs after discharge home. Ms. B is clearly upset about the wide disagreement among family members regarding the experimental treatment. The team realizes that the goals of the meeting must be broadened to include discussion of the next stage in treatment, the Phase I drug, as well as advance care planning and setting Ms. B's goals for care. She needs assistance in navigating the complex demands of her illness, making decisions about treatment, and communicating with her family.

INTERVENTION STRATEGY: THE FAMILY MEETING

Prior to the meeting, the palliative care social worker speaks to the eldest daughter and realizes that she has limited knowledge about her mother's increasing frailty and poor prognosis, and lacks understanding of her mother's preferences for care. Unfortunately, the daughter is unable to attend the meeting in person, but will participate by telephone.

The family meeting is attended by Ms. B, all four children (one by phone), her sisters, the oncologist, the palliative care physician, nurse, and social worker, each with his or her own agenda. Ms. B's children hope to convince Ms. B to accept chemotherapy. The sisters believe Ms. B should decline chemotherapy and appoint a different healthcare agent. The oncologist is torn about offering chemotherapy, but prefers to maintain hope and possibly extend Ms. B's life. The palliative care team wants to explore the family's understanding about the disease and prognosis, and develop a plan that supports her goals of care.

The palliative care social worker opens the meeting and introductions are shared. The oncologist gives a medical update, reviews the illness progression, and acknowledges they have now reached a fork in the road. He mentions experimental chemotherapy as an option, if Ms. B is "willing to give it a try." The palliative care physician gives his perspective, highlighting Ms. B's symptom burden and introducing the option of hospice care to provide ongoing support as well as expertise in symptom control.

Ms. B's children urge their mother to accept the Phase I drug. Ms. B's sisters disagree, favoring a more "natural approach." They further state that prognostic information cannot be trusted because "the future is in God's hands and no one can predict the future." In addition, they express their belief Ms. B's daughter is a poor choice for healthcare agent, as she is too young and not wise enough to make the right decisions, especially long-distance. Before the oncologist can respond, a loud argument ensues.

Finally, the palliative physician asks for quiet so Ms. B can speak. Ms. B, initially confused by conflicting information from the different medical teams, has ultimately decided to forgo the proposed experimental chemotherapy. She states she knows she is dying and wants to know "how long" she has. If time is short, she would like to spend time with family and friends, and create a legacy project for the grandchildren she will never meet. Based on her discussion with the palliative care team, she states that she would like to sign onto hospice home care, and the oncologist says he supports her decision. Ms. B seems relieved, stating this is her preference, and her family "will have to get used to it." Ms. B's sisters are in favor of hospice, while her children seem more ambivalent and "not yet ready to give up." They do not have much knowledge about hospice and express concern that Ms. B will have to move to a facility where they won't be able to visit her. The palliative care team arranges a second meeting to discuss the Medicare Hospice Benefit and hospice enrollment in more detail and give the family an opportunity to digest the information.

CONCLUSIONS AND REFLECTIONS

The palliative care team called the family meeting to help Ms. B clarify the goals of care and enlist her family's understanding and support. The team hoped that the meeting would offer a vehicle to provide support to the family, mitigate the divisive nature of their discussions, and move towards consensus. The strategy included providing clear information about risks and benefits of treatment, conveying the seriousness of the disease, and assuring the family of non-abandonment. The palliative care team hoped to validate the family's emotional responses and support their efforts to cope with a devastating prognosis. However, they were unable to achieve professional consensus in a pre-meeting with the oncologist and they became aware of high levels of conflict among family members. These challenges had to be managed during the meeting.

Family conflict takes many forms, highlighting individual differences in emotional resilience, beliefs, and decision making. Generational and cultural conflicts must be understood as family consensus is sought. Mediating conflict involves assessment of a family's medical literacy, including their understanding of treatment options and likely disease trajectory. A family's experience with prior cancer therapy and closeness to the patient provides a lens through which the current situation is seen. Because these discussions are complex, advance care planning discussions cannot be rushed.

The perceptions and differing expertise of the oncology and palliative care teams must be integrated, as each brings a different perspective to the meeting. It is unhelpful to have professional disagreements in front of the family. The palliative care team must maintain its position as a consultant but be prepared to take more responsibility as the goals of care shift. It is always optimal to achieve professional consensus, but if this is not possible, respectful dialogue is a useful compromise.

Lastly, a patient with capacity such as Ms. B must be heard; it may be easy to discount the opinion of a frail patient. The patient should be supported in her decision making and given a voice.

Myra Glajchen, DSW, is director of medical education at the MJHS Institute for Innovation in Palliative Care where she is responsible for the education and training of physicians and other disciplines. She is assistant professor of Family and Social Medicine at Albert Einstein College of Medicine and associate program director of the Fellowship Training Program. Dr. Glajchen is nationally known for her work in caregiver burden and palliative care. At Beth Israel, she created the Family Caregiver Initiative to improve the well-being of caregivers facing advanced illness, developed clinical initiatives, and led the research team that validated the Brief Assessment Scale for Caregivers (BASC) in English and Chinese. Dr. Glajchen is co-investigator for a transitional care planning study for the frail elderly, Improving Patient and Caregiver Well-being via Hospital-Community Linkages and an Enhanced Communications Strategy for

Transitional Care Planning. She is co-editor for The Oxford Textbook of Palliative Care Communication; *book review editor for* The Journal of Pain and Symptom Management; *associate editor of PC-FACS, American Academy of Hospice and Palliative Medicine; and a member of the PDQ Supportive Care Board of the National Cancer Institute.*

Maj Eisinger, MD, FACEP, *is a fellow in the MJHS Hospice and Palliative Care Fellowship program. She is a graduate of the University of California, San Francisco School of Medicine and a diplomate of the American Board of Internal Medicine and the American Board of Emergency Medicine. Dr. Eisinger is a fellow in the American College of Emergency Physicians. She is an associate professor in the Department of Surgery at the University of Vermont Medical Center, where she practices emergency medicine.*

References

Arber, A. (2015). Team communication in the hospice setting. In E. Wittenberg-Lyles, B. Ferrell, J. Goldsmith, T. Smith, S. Egan, M. Glajchen, & G. Handzo (Eds.), *Oxford textbook of palliative care communication* (pp. 340-345). Oxford, UK: Oxford University Press.

Chou, W. S., Gaysynsky, A., & Persoskie, A. (2015). Health literacy and communication in palliative care. In E. Wittenberg-Lyles, B. Ferrell, J. Goldsmith, T. Smith, S. Egan, M. Glajchen, & G. Handzo (Eds.), *Oxford textbook of palliative care communication* (pp. 90-101). Oxford, UK: Oxford University Press.

Curtis, J. R., Patrick, D. L., Shannon, S. E., Treece, P. D., Engelberg R. A., & Rubenfeld, G. D. (2001). The family conference as a focus to improve communication about end-of-life care in the intensive care unit: Opportunities for improvement. *Critical Care Medicine, 29*(2 Suppl), 26-33.

Dean, M. & Street, R. L. (2015). Patient-centered communication. In E. Wittenberg-Lyles, B. Ferrell, J. Goldsmith, T. Smith, S. Egan, M. Glajchen, & G. Handzo (Eds.), *Oxford textbook of palliative care communication* (pp. 238-245). Oxford, UK: Oxford University Press.

Hannon, B., O'Reilly, V., Bennett, K., Breen, K., & Lawlor, P. G. (2012). Meeting the family: Measuring effectiveness of family meetings in a specialist inpatient palliative care unit. *Palliative &*

Supportive Care, 10(1), 43-49.

Hirschman, K. B., Corcoran, A. M., Straton, J. B., & Kapo, J. M. (2010). Advance care planning and hospice enrollment: Who really makes the decision to enroll? *Journal of Palliative Medicine, May 13*(5), 519-523.

Palos, G. R. (2015). Cultural considerations in palliative care and serious illness. In E. Wittenberg-Lyles, B. Ferrell, J. Goldsmith, T. Smith, S. Egan, M. Glajchen, & G. Handzo (Eds.), *Oxford textbook of palliative care communication* (pp. 153-160). Oxford, UK: Oxford University Press.

Sharma, R. K. & Dy, S. M. (2011). Cross-cultural communication and use of the family meeting in palliative care. *American Journal of Hospice & Palliative Medicine, 28*(6). 437-444.

CHAPTER 5

A Request for Nondisclosure of Hospice Care

Kenneth J. Doka

CASE DESCRIPTION

Mr. Martinez is a 66-year-old who has late-stage lung cancer. An immigrant from Guatemala, Mr. Martinez worked as a skilled automotive repairman at a major dealership until he retired early at the age of 62, after his cancer diagnosis. He was referred to hospice care by his oncologist who suggested it to his wife and daughters after stating "there was nothing more that medicine could do for him." Mr. Martinez's wife requested services from the hospice but asked the staff to not tell her husband that he is in the final stage of his illness. She also requested that if Mr. Martinez asks where the staff works, they should say they are home health providers and not use the word "hospice." Mr. Martinez is supported by a small but close family including his wife, two married daughters and their families, and a younger brother who is a Catholic priest in the community. Father Joe is well-respected by the hospice chaplain for his pastoral services and devotion to parishioners who have been in hospice care.

STATEMENT OF PROBLEM

Mrs. Martinez made it clear that she does not want her husband to know he is receiving hospice care. How should a hospice respond to a request for nondisclosure when that is posed as a condition for accepting hospice care? Part of the problem in this particular case is illustrated by the oncologist's comment that hospice was appropriate because "there was nothing more that medicine could do for him." Such reasoning, however common, does a considerable disservice to hospice and palliative care which have much to offer, including pain management, symptom control, holistic and family-centered care, and a team approach to treatment. A better approach would have been to begin with a discussion of the family's hopes and goals for the patient. In that discussion, it would be critical for the family to fully understand and accept that the goal of care now was palliative; medical interventions could no longer offer a cure or an extension of life, but there was much that could be done to ease death. Such discussion should be done sensitively, acknowledging the family's hopes for a different outcome, while affirming much could be offered to make Mr. Martinez's final days more comfortable and to support his family.

ANALYSIS

Nondisclosure requests to hospice are not unusual (Partington & Kirk, 2015). Partington and Kirk (2015) make a persuasive case that granting nondisclosure requests is inimical to effective hospice care. Patient-centered care is central to the hospice philosophy, they argue. In order for care to be effective and suffering minimized, an individual's experience of dying needs to be integrated within his or her life experience. By that, the authors mean patients needing to discuss their impending deaths or review their lives as they face death should be able to do so. This process can only occur in a context where there is open communication—that is, care that is not bound in secrecy.

In addition, Partington and Kirk (2015) acknowledge the ethical argument for disclosure. Truthfulness requires that patients have the requisite information to make decisions; beneficence and sensitivity require, to Partington and Kirk, that the process of obtaining the family's consent for disclosure may involve patience and time, entailing active listening and a shared commitment to benefit the patient, as well as acknowledgment and validation of the emotions of family caregivers. But the end result is that patients should have full knowledge of their state.

However, such a position needs to concede that different cultures have different stances toward disclosure. Years ago, I had the opportunity to do some work around grief and loss with the Iñupiat peoples, a Native Alaskan group. The Iñupiat place great value on words. One of the ethical issues experienced by professionals working with this population was that many times individuals would refuse to sign advance care directives after a discussion of the possible situations that can occur during serious illness, injury, or death. In Iñupiat culture, talk of illness, injury, or death is believed to be a bad omen that has real potential to cause such adversity to occur.

While there are significant cultural differences, diverse ethnicities, and varied experiences within the Hispanic cultures, some of the values common to this culture influence the decision on how to respond to the Martinez family's request for nondisclosure. First is the value of *familismo*, which recognizes the importance of family ties and relationships and places the locus of decision making within the family rather than the individual. Second is a value of *presentismo*, or an emphasis on the present; one should live in the moment as one never knows what the future will bring. Within this perspective is a strain of fatalism expressed by the common expression *que sera, sera*, or *what will be, will be*. Such values can inhibit advance care planning as well as discussions of death (Houben, 2012; Talamantes, Gomez, & Braun, 2000).

GOALS OF COUNSELING

Truth-telling is different from *truth-offering*. It is one thing to demand that patients face the truth whether they wish to hear it or not; it is quite another to offer patients information *if* they wish to hear it. The goal of palliative care should be one of *open communication*. Open communication begins with a goal to keep the conversation going; that one truthfully responds to questions patients ask in ways that assess what the patient is really asking, and provides answers in such that dialogue is not closed.

My own family's experience offers a good example of this. My father had excellent care in hospice, yet there was one conversation I wish would have been handled differently. Dad knew both his diagnosis and terminal prognosis. He understood that he was in hospice care, fully knowing what that meant. Yet one day, even though he was bedbound, he asked his nurse when she thought he might drive again. She seemed shocked by the question and reminded my father that he was dying and would never be able to drive. My father held his anger but, from that moment on, conversations with her were merely perfunctory. I wish the nurse would have not focused so much on "truth-telling," and focused instead on addressing his loss (*You really must miss driving*) or assess for any unfinished business (*If you could drive, where would you like to go?*).

Open communication requires understanding the reality of *middle knowledge* (Weisman, 1972). Middle knowledge means that while most patients recognize that they are dying, responding to both internal and external cues as well as their own knowledge, they often drift in and out of the awareness. Sometimes they will acknowledge the situation, other times they choose to ignore the closeness of death. Understanding middle knowledge means that clinicians recognize that individuals who are dying will choose the times, places, and persons with whom they share their questions and concerns.

INTERVENTION STRATEGY

When Mr. Martinez's family made the request for nondisclosure, the hospice team first convened a meeting with an ethics consult to discuss the family's concerns and needs. They then invited Mr. Martinez's family to a meeting with the hospice team. Family members who attended included Mr. Martinez's wife, two daughters, a son-in-law, and Mr. Martinez's brother, Father Joe. The family expressed a concern that if Mr. Martinez knew he was dying, he would lose all hope, withdraw from the family, and die more quickly. While Father Joe functioned as the family spokesperson, it was evident that he felt somewhat discomforted by the family's position.

The hospice team first carefully listened to the family's concerns and validated their caring. The team then shared their own philosophy of open communication. They assured the family that they would address prognosis only if and when Mr. Martinez brought up the issue, after carefully exploring his questions, and with the aim of continuing a dialogue until his concerns were met. Throughout this process, Father Joe acted as mediator, reminding his family that past work with hospice patients gave him great confidence in the care this hospice could provide. The team suggested a follow-up meeting in two weeks; although tentative, the family agreed, and hospice services were started.

Mr. Martinez politely declined chaplaincy services, proudly affirming that his spiritual needs would be taken care of by his "kid brother, who is also a wonderful priest." Mr. Martinez was quiet and rarely asked questions or expressed needs to his social worker, nurse, or physician.

Family members seemed guarded around the professional staff; however, the team discovered that Mr. Martinez had had extensive conversations with Anita, his home health aide, about his concerns for his family after he died. Father Joe later found out that the aide possessed two attributes that facilitated conversation: as a Puerto Rican native, she was fluent in Spanish, and the family often used the time that she was there to do chores, allowing Mr. Martinez and Anita time to talk alone. Father Joe realized that while his brother was aware of his prognosis, he found it difficult to discuss death with his family, and sought to protect them.

At the second meeting with the hospice team, both Mr. Martinez and Anita participated. Hearing this, the family realized that that they, too, could more openly address issues related to dying. The hospice also provided a Spanish-speaking nurse, adding another level of comfort. While discussions of death never predominated, it was no longer a taboo topic. In fact, Mr. Martinez and his brother began to plan his funeral, sometimes even making jokes about the plans. Within 10 weeks of entering hospice, Mr. Martinez died peacefully with his wife and brother by his side.

CONCLUSIONS AND REFLECTIONS

The story of the Martinez family reaffirms that cultural issues can play a large role in both the acceptance of hospice care and the way dying is viewed and discussed. The fact that Mr. Martinez accepted hospice care is interesting, as Hispanics and Latinos, especially first generation, are underrepresented in hospice (Talamantes et al., 2000); recent data shows that only 7.1% of hospice patients were of Hispanic or Latino origin (NHPCO, 2015). Having literature, community liaisons, and staff that can communicate in the language of varied cultures within the community, as well as sensitivity to cultural nuances around death and dying, are essential for outreach into underserved populations.

Cultural sensitivity training of hospice teams should include home health aides, often representative of these same underserved populations. As with Anita and Mr. Martinez, home health aides often develop close relationships with patients and may therefore have critical information that the patient has only shared with them. This situation is reflective of the Hispanic cultural value of *personalismo*, which places a high value on personal relationships and mutual disclosure; families may be intimidated by doctors and nurses, in part because the time they spend with the patient may focus primarily on medical issues and may therefore be perceived as somewhat distant.

Another important point is that there is a difference between truth-telling and open communication. Hospices should train staff in the open communication approach, as it is sensitive to cultural differences and constraints regarding conversations about death. This approach is also consistent with middle knowledge, offering patients control of whether, when, how, and with whom they choose to communicate their fears and anxieties about death.

It seems clear that hospices can function most effectively when there is open communication among patients, families, and staff. If families wish to deny or discourage an open communicative process, it is difficult to see how effective care can be offered. In such circumstances, hospices should decline care in all but the most extraordinary situations, such as a patient's extreme anxiety or diminished capacity to process such information. Open communication, after all, is the gold, silver, and bronze standard of care.

Kenneth J. Doka, PhD, MDiv, *is a professor of gerontology at the Graduate School of The College of New Rochelle and senior consultant to Hospice Foundation of America. Dr. Doka serves as editor of HFA's* Living with Grief® *book series, its* Journeys *newsletter, and numerous other books and publications. Dr. Doka has served as a panelist on HFA's* Living with Grief® *video programs for 22 years. He is a past president of the Association for Death Education and Counseling (ADEC) and received the Special Contributions Award in the field of Death Education from the Association for Death Education and Counseling. He is a member and past chair of the International Work Group on Death, Dying and Bereavement. In 2006, Dr. Doka was grandfathered in as a mental health counselor under New York's first state licensure of counselors. Dr. Doka is an ordained Lutheran minister.*

References

Hoeben, L. (2012). *Counseling Hispanics through grief, loss, and bereavement.* New York, NY: Springer.

National Hospice and Palliative Care Organization. (2015). *NHPCO Facts and Figures: Hospice Care in America.* Alexandria, VA: National Hospice and Palliative Care Organization.

Partington, E. W., & Kirk, T. (2015). Engaging requests for nondisclosure during admission to home hospice care. *Journal of Hospice and Palliative Nursing, 17*, 174-181.

Talamantes, M., Gomez, C., & Braun, K. (2000). Advance directives and end-of-life care: An Hispanic perspective. In K. L. Braun, J. H. Pietsch, & P. L Blanchette (Eds.), *Cultural issues in end-of-life decision making* (pp. 83-100). Thousand Oaks, CA: Sage.

Weisman, A. (1972). *On dying and denying: A psychiatric study of terminality.* New York, NY: Behavioral Publications.

CHAPTER 6

The Importance of Culturally Competent Family Meetings

Sherry R. Schachter and Raman Randhawa

Effective communication is an essential factor in creating a therapeutic environment when providing effective hospice care. For families and friends faced with end-of-life challenges and decisions that, for most, they never envisioned, clarity and understanding of the goals of care are crucial.

Most families want to make decisions on what they believe is best for the individual; however, it is often the case that family members may have different beliefs as to how they define and determine what "the best" actually is. Disagreements may arise because the history and narrative with the dying person are viewed from different perspectives. Ensuring that a loved one's death is the very best it could be will impact both the patient and the bereavement outcome. As families review or reflect about end-of-life care they often focus on their role in decision making, and regrets and feelings of guilt can often impede their bereavement journey.

Honoring and respecting the many viewpoints brought to the table is a skill that can be taught and reinforced. Encouraging patient and family meetings allows everyone to come together. Skilled clinicians who guide these meetings create an environment that is open and caring, encouraging members to participate; ensuring that every voice is heard, even a dissenting one, is essential. The following case exemplifies the importance of effective communication in allowing the family to come together despite their differences and desires while also respecting their cultural beliefs.

CASE DESCRIPTION

JR was a 78-year-old Indian husband and father of three adult children. He had a history of metastatic colon cancer and diabetes. Several of his toes (on both feet) had been amputated because of his uncontrolled diabetes. JR lived at home with his frail wife who had recently been diagnosed with dementia. Both sons lived an hour away and his youngest, his only daughter, lived out of state with her partner and young children. While all three children were involved in their parents' care, there was dissension among them as to what that care should be. JR had undergone a surgical resection and despite numerous courses of chemotherapy his disease was progressing. During one of his many hospitalizations his physician recommended home hospice care. Although the physician gave a general description of hospice, it was unclear if JR or his children actually fully understood what hospice was. He was discharged home from the hospital and hospice care was initiated. Due to his wife's frail condition, JR's home hospice care was administered at their oldest son's home.

Despite an initial disagreement between the hospice nurse and the eldest son, the first days and weeks of JR's care went relatively smoothly. Home visits were made by the nurse and soon a therapeutic and warm relationship was formed. JR's oldest son was appointed as his primary caregiver (PCG). It is a common Indian cultural belief that it is the responsibility of the oldest son to take care of his aging parents. This expected responsibility is taught early on and is known and understood by all members within the household. The son was attentive to his father's needs and would frequently call the hospice nurse with questions regarding blood work, lab results, and requests for physical and occupational therapy. Initially, JR refused the offer for social work visits, saying they were not needed. This hesitation and refusal may have been due to cultural beliefs or a sense of mistrust for a caregiver who is not familiar with the specific beliefs of the Indian culture. There are many cultures where the primary means of support are strongly rooted in faith and family dynamics. In this case, the PCG and patient finally agreed to see an Indian priest, provided by the hospice team, who had ties with other Indian priests from the community who provide per diem services. The Indian priest came regularly and soon developed rapport with the patient. In time, with the urging of the Indian priest, the patient and PCG allowed the social worker to visit. This was a pivotal juncture in the patient's care.

STATEMENT OF PROBLEM

Immediately after discharge from the hospital, JR was visited by the hospice nurse who took a detailed history. She ordered JR's medications and explained they would be delivered later in the day. JR's son was present when the medications were delivered. He became enraged when he noticed that there was only a two-week supply. He called and screamed at the nurse, *"Do you think my dad is only going to live two weeks? Why did you not give him a three-month supply?"* The nurse tried to explain her rationale, noting that because medications often need to be changed frequently, it would be beneficial to order them as they needed them. She was able to reassure the son that all medication changes would be delivered by the pharmacy in a timely way.

The patient's wife, because of her dementia, did not participate in decision making. Initially, JR was able to voice what he wanted ("no social worker," "okay for the priest to come"); however, as his disease progressed and he became weaker, JR became quieter and more withdrawn, leaving decisions to his children. Although it was understood that all decisions were to eventually be made by the oldest son, the siblings were conflicted in what they wanted for their father. The daughter visited every other week and did not want to see her father suffering and in pain any longer. She felt that it would be best to discontinue what she saw as aggressive treatment, including bloodwork or chest x-rays, even though her elder brother wanted these to continue. The middle sibling would visit daily while juggling his responsibilities of work and his own family.

Although all the siblings had varying views on how to continue care for their father, they also struggled with making a decision in his best interest while juggling cultural views on end-of-life care. According to this family's cultural view on medical care and death, there was an importance placed on taking a holistic approach to decision making. In the past, decisions had generally been made as a family, incorporating their varied religious and cultural views. Although this was an intact family, disagreements among the siblings arose as their father continued to decline. The oldest son believed that because his father was always a "fighter" who had overcome many obstacles when he came to this country, they needed to ensure that he continue "to fight." The son often described his father as "his hero," noting how he pushed himself despite several amputations. The oldest son did not agree with his sister's belief that discontinuing their father's treatment would be the best decision, and insisted on frequent blood work and other medical interventions.

Although JR was on hospice care his PCG, the eldest son, did not agree to a Do Not Resuscitate (DNR) status. Instead, he wanted his father's primary care physician to continue to monitor his father's blood work, and requested chest x-rays when the patient became short of breath. The middle son was ambivalent, struggling between the beliefs of his sister and the decision-making responsibility of his older brother. While the siblings understood that the elder son was the primary caregiver and the legal health care proxy and that his decisions were binding, the friction among them was painful to observe. Upon admission to hospice, this family reported being very close and always supportive of one another; now, as JR was rapidly declining, they were barely speaking to one another.

GOALS OF COUNSELING

During weekly hospice interdisciplinary team meetings the staff struggled with ways to help the family come to terms with JR's impending death. It was decided that a family meeting would be beneficial so that the siblings could voice their concerns and hopefully come to a resolution. As with most families, end-of-life discussions are challenging and stressful. The authors' experience has been that one family meeting is generally not sufficient to meet the needs of a family. Despite frequent home visits by members of the hospice team, JR and his family required several interdisciplinary meetings to ensure that everyone's voice was heard and therapeutic interventions could be described and incorporated into the plan of care.

ANALYSIS

The major issues for this family included these concerns.

- The siblings did not want their father to suffer, however, the eldest son continued to ask for unnecessary tests and treatment (e.g., blood work, intravenous fluids, etc.) while the two other siblings expressed wanting to focus more on palliative care and keeping their father comfortable.
- In thinking ahead, the family and hospice team were facing struggles with decisions about feeding JR.
- The family was unsure as to how they could care for their father in a "traditional" way honoring his religious and cultural beliefs,

and feared they would be unable to respect their parents' wishes to die at home.
- The siblings were nervous and unsure about how and what to tell their extended family so that they could come and visit their father.
- The oldest son had overall anxiety about his responsibility in "doing the right thing."

INTERVENTION STRATEGIES

The family meetings were held at the eldest son's home since this is where JR's home hospice care was administered. During one of the meetings a telephone conference call was initiated so that JR's daughter, who was unable to travel that particular day, would be able to participate. This involvement was essential, as it allowed all the siblings to hear information at the same time and to listen to all the responses and engage in the discussion. The hospice team on the call included the physician, the primary nurse, social worker, and the patient's Indian priest. JR's children were united in insisting that both their father and mother not be present for the meetings (the mother had limited understanding because of her dementia; JR was too frail and he deferred all decisions to his eldest son). Therefore, arrangements were made for a hospice volunteer to be present and she was instrumental in occupying JR and his wife in another room while the family meeting occurred.

Everyone sat around the dining room table while the son's wife served tea, coffee, and cake, and insisted they have some refreshments. The hospice physician then took the lead and explained in detail JR's prognosis and progression of disease. A few times during these meetings the physician would go into great lengths with his explanation, sometimes confusing the siblings. JR's social worker took the role of clarifying and summarizing the salient points.

The meetings provided a framework for the hospice team to address the concerns of JR's children. The team felt it was a challenge to balance being respectful to the oldest son (the PCG) but also to include the concerns of the two other siblings in the sensitive discussions. The siblings explained their concerns, noting that they only wanted what was best for their father. They politely but firmly shared that they were "overwhelmed" with their father's care and by their concern for their mother, who did not fully understand what was happening. The siblings said that they had not told their large, extended family about their father's condition because they worried that the family would come to see their father to say their goodbyes. The oldest son expressed not being sure how his mother would react to seeing so many people; he didn't know what to say to them. He was torn because he knew that his father would want to see his family before he died, and it was equally important for his loved ones to see him. Hearing this, the social worker encouraged the siblings to contact all the extended family members to give them the opportunity to visit and support the family. She offered to help the siblings, giving them the words they would need.

JR's Indian priest talked about end-of-life decisions as they related to their parents' cultural beliefs. Everyone was given a chance to talk, ask questions, and explain their feelings. Although the siblings were not religious, they respected their parents' religious beliefs and culture and acknowledged that familiar rituals would be a source of comfort to them. The priest was a significant presence in the meeting as he explained the appropriate religious rituals in very concrete terms and developed a plan to implement these rituals at the son's home. While the priest was clear that he could not participate in the 24-hour prayers required, he developed a plan to help forge an alliance within the local Indian community, ensuring that JR would be prayed over prior to his death. After death, another priest from the local Indian community would conduct prayers in the son's home for a three-day period. Members of their extended family and community would be invited to sit and pray with the family at the home, ensuring that JR would have a peaceful sendoff into the next world.

Understanding the significance of having JR die at home and not in a hospital, the nurse and physician explained to the siblings how they could keep their father comfortable by arranging to have a "comfort pack" delivered to the house with the medications JR might need as he neared death. They reiterated that whenever the siblings felt a need to call the team for additional emotional support, they could call the 24-hour number and know that an actual nurse, not an answering service, would be available to help.

One of the challenges the family and the hospice team struggled with was the decision regarding feeding JR. As do many families, the siblings viewed giving their father food as a way of showing their love and respect for him; not giving him hydration was unthinkable. The family asked many questions regarding their father's nutrition, including the use of artificial nutrition and hydration through a feeding tube. While the hospice staff patiently discussed the various medical aspects and potential risks of providing nutrition in this way, the social worker and Indian priest offered different ways for them to show their love and respect.

With the emotional support of the social worker, the patient's eldest son eventually recognized JR's decline. He wanted an opportunity to talk with his father, to ascertain his father's awareness, his fears, or regrets he may have had. The son recognized that he was unable to have these conversations because of JR's mental limitations. Due to the son's upbringing and the family dynamics, he was uncomfortable because these were not things the family discussed. This was a family that found it uncomfortable to speak of one's distressed emotional state and vulnerability. The son felt that he had a responsibility and obligation to always appear stoic as he was the eldest. Once again, the social worker provided emotional support to the son by initiating opportunities for him to express, vent, and manage his feelings in private sessions. Also with the help of the social worker, he was able to use writing techniques to express his regrets and fears of having the responsibility for making end-of-life decisions on his father's behalf.

CONCLUSIONS AND REFLECTIONS

Healthcare providers care for patients from diverse religious and cultural backgrounds. It is crucial that these professionals be aware of various belief systems to provide a context for understanding the experiences of dying patients and their family members. As was the case with the interdisciplinary team meetings for JR and his family, a team's shared understanding of cultural beliefs may help prevent potential conflicts and facilitate effective communication with the family members and staff. These meetings promoted ongoing educational support to help the siblings recognize all that they were doing to care for their father. The meetings enabled the family to come together and create a plan of care that was sustainable and reflected their values and cultural beliefs. Additionally, careful attention was given to situations where private sessions were necessary for JR's oldest son to work through some of the guilt and regrets he was experiencing. The family was reassured that cultural rituals would be observed to respect their beliefs and align with their grieving process. Although JR's adult children differed in their viewpoints on end-of-life care for their father, the skilled clinicians were able to guide family meetings by creating an open and caring environment where all voices were heard and respected.

Providing Culturally Competent Care at the End of Life

- Pay attention to the body language of patient and family members. There may be signals that the person is distressed but hesitant to discuss or initiate the conversation. This reticence to discuss end-of-life issues may come from a family or cultural perspective; the clinician should be aware of the source of their hesitance in order to provide appropriate therapeutic intervention.
- Use open-ended questions, requiring more than a simple yes or no, to further your understanding and clarify your assumptions.
- Appreciate the patient's culture by providing care that incorporates the individual's values, cultural, and religious beliefs.
- Remain nonjudgmental when given information that reflects values that differ from yours.
- Know the patient's wishes regarding communication, i.e., directly with the hospice team, or with the person of his or her choice, such as a partner or adult child.

Sherry R. Schachter, PhD, FT, is the director of bereavement services for Calvary Hospital/Hospice where she develops, coordinates, and facilitates educational services for staff, and develops and oversees an extensive bereavement program. She is also the director of Camp Compass®, a summer camp for bereaved children and teens. Dr. Schachter is a recipient of the prestigious Lane Adams Award for Excellence in Cancer Nursing from the American Cancer Society. She is a past president of the Association for Death Education and Counseling (ADEC) and is a member of the International Work Group on Death, Dying, and Bereavement.

Raman Randhawa, LMHC, NCC, has a degree in Clinical Mental Health Counseling from St. John's University and is currently enrolled in the Counselor Education Doctoral program at Montclair State University. She is a licensed mental health counselor and holds recognition as a National Certified Counselor (NCC). She is currently practicing as a bereavement counselor at Calvary Hospital where she runs adult bereavement groups.

CHAPTER 7

Gilbert and Edwin: Life and Death Transitions

Doneley Meris

CASE DESCRIPTION

Gilbert, a 47-year-old philosophy professor and Edwin, a 43-year-old sculptor and graphic designer, have been lovers for eight years. While they maintain separate apartments in New York City, their lives are joined in almost every other way. They co-own a colonial two-story home in upstate New York; they travel together, share a circle of close friends, and have interconnected their finances.

Gilbert was infected with HIV/AIDS prior to meeting Edwin when a mutual friend introduced them. Edwin revealed that he was HIV-negative during their first date, yet he wanted to pursue a relationship with Gilbert. Their HIV-discordant status was not initially an issue, but as they became sexually involved, Gilbert was very concerned about infecting his partner, while Edwin realized that he might not have a satisfying sexual life with the constant reminder of being with an HIV-positive man.

They decided to pursue couples counseling to figure out how to make sense of their increasing barriers to genuine physical and emotional intimacy. With assistance from a clinician associated with an HIV-services agency, Gilbert and Edwin participated in short-term couples therapy, exploring their fears, sexual anxieties, and cognitive hindrances to a gratifying intimacy. By openly communicating the elements of their sexual connection, they mutually agreed to continue nurturing their loving ties.

Another issue discovered through this therapeutic process that was a barrier to their relationship was their disclosure-discordance. Edwin was open about being a gay man, and soon after meeting Gilbert, promptly introduced him to his friends and his two siblings. After three months of dating, he brought Gilbert to a party at his parents' home, introducing him as his new boyfriend, and has included Gilbert in all of his family's gatherings since. Gilbert, on the other hand, has not come out to his family. His parents and sister live in a small town in North Carolina, and although he suspected that they knew about his sexual orientation, they have maintained a "don't ask" stance. Gilbert spoke to his parents by phone occasionally and always spent time with them over the holidays. Edwin related this familial-social disconnect during their counseling sessions and requested an additional two sessions to make sense of this disengagement.

Reluctantly, Gilbert admitted to his fears not only of revealing his gay identity but also his HIV-positive status to his religious and socially-connected parents. He asked Edwin to be more patient, promising to eventually disclose his "dual identity" to his family, and requested acknowledgment of his struggle. Edwin voiced his support but reiterated that this issue would continue to be the "elephant in the room" in their union.

Three years after completing couples counseling, Gilbert and Edwin solidified their relationship by jointly increasing their financial portfolio and purchasing another apartment. Despite passage of a same-sex marriage law in the state of New York, they agreed that marriage was not yet in the cards for them, though they left the door open in their future. Gilbert had still not shared anything with his family about his life with Edwin.

STATEMENT OF PROBLEM

In August 2014, Gilbert was hospitalized with a relatively minor sinus infection. But he had an allergic reaction to one of his medications, resulting in respiratory failure that required he be put on a ventilator. Somehow, the charge nurse overlooked information in Gilbert's patient file listing Edwin as his emergency contact and called Gilbert's parents in North Carolina instead.

Gilbert's parents arrived in New York City the next evening and were puzzled to meet Edwin at Gilbert's bedside. Edwin introduced himself as their son's partner and began to explain the delicate status of their son's health. Gilbert's parents were shocked—simultaneously dealing with learning of their son's sexuality, his HIV status, his partner, and the impending medical emergency. Gilbert's father projected the anger at his son toward Edwin, immediately instructing him to leave the room and sternly requesting the hospital refuse Edwin any further access. Edwin told hospital administrators that he was a member of Gilbert's "family" and refused to be kept away from his partner's care. Security guards were called and he was relegated to the lobby.[1]

Although Gilbert had planned to do so, he never filled out a medical directive authorizing Edwin to oversee his medical care and end-of-life wishes. Because he was now under heavy sedation, Gilbert's parents became responsible for his care decisions. While Edwin remained in the hospital lobby, Gilbert's parents left for a local hotel. Early the next morning, Gilbert's condition worsened; he suffered cardiac arrest and was declared dead. Gilbert's parents were called back to the hospital, but Edwin, still at the hospital, was not allowed near his partner's room and was not permitted to say goodbye to his long-time partner. Gilbert's parents quickly arranged for the body to be transported to their hometown, where Gilbert was buried in the family plot two days later. Edwin did not participate in the plans or the ceremony.

ANALYSIS

Although Edwin was comforted by his family and huge circle of friends, and was offered assistance from two friends who were lawyers, he was distraught, angry, and traumatized. He decided to call the counselor he and Gilbert had worked with during their early relational challenges. Edwin's grief, though supported by others in the friendship circle, was disenfranchised by Gilbert's family and the hospital staff. This disenfranchisement, which included the lack of opportunity to mourn with Gilbert's parents or to offer a final goodbye, complicated Edwin's grief. Edwin shared that he wanted to make sense of how heartlessly Gilbert's family had treated him and the overwhelming grief over his partner's death.

GOALS OF COUNSELING

Edwin recognized that he needed support in processing his grief over Gilbert's death and the events that preceded it. He also sought

---

1 Federal guidelines mandate hospitals that participate in Medicare and Medicaid provide visitation rights to domestic partners of incapacitated patients without requiring documentation of those relationships in most circumstances. However, it is recognized that many times such directives may not be fully followed (Riou, 2014).

counseling in an attempt to find meaning in Gilbert's death and to understand his life purpose in his new role as a bereaved partner.

INTERVENTION STRATEGY

Edwin began seeing the counselor two or three times a week for grief-life transitions counseling. He was closely monitored by his medical practitioner and a psychiatric nurse, identifying his family-social support networks with a hierarchical guideline of contacts and outreach, and a framework of procedural actions for his physical safety-comfort. Multiple monitors were employed to assure his safety controls and social ties over a period of six weeks.

In his individual grief-life transitions counseling work, Edwin was allowed to review his intense and loving connection with Gilbert; slowly face the reality of life without him; cope with continued and painful lack of contact with Gilbert's family; deal with the financial and legal ramifications Gilbert's death had on their property and finances; and redefine his life as an HIV-negative gay man. He even planned a memorial service for Gilbert that was well attended by colleagues from Gilbert's college and friends within and outside of their gay community.

Edwin also agreed to participate in a 10-week grief support group with five other gay men who lost their partners. He was able to hear the challenges and daily adjustments others courageously took to be reintegrated with their gay community and their supportive networks. Edwin was reserved with what he shared, but during his individual counseling sessions he acknowledged that it was helpful for him to discover from the voices of others that his future alone was linked to his personal and incremental efforts to reconnect with his unpredictable world. Four months after Gilbert's death, Edwin completed his participation in the grief support group and decided to be seen individually every two weeks instead of several times a week. He realigned his support networks and found the courage to go back to his studio to create art again. His remarkable embrace of living was reinforced and fully supported by his counselor and support group.

CONCLUSIONS AND REFLECTIONS

Edwin's case is an excellent example of some of the challenges posed to gay couples. While same-sex marriage is now legal, gay partners still face discrimination in asserting their rights. This case also reaffirms the necessity to have legal documents in place that could have forestalled Edwin's exclusion from Gilbert's care.

Edwin's role and grief were disenfranchised by Gilbert's family. Disenfranchised grief refers to losses that are not acknowledged by others, socially sanctioned, or publicly mourned (Doka, 2002). While the parents disenfranchised Edwin's grief, the counselor, support group, and later, the memorial service, validated Edwin's role in Gilbert's life and legitimized Edwin's grief.

The case of Edwin and Gilbert is both a challenge and a refrain for many gay men as they navigate complex realities. Death is a complicated journey that touches human and humane processes. Key to survival is recapturing the energy to live, reincorporating remembrances and memories of the deceased into daily life encounters, and sustaining the desire to make a difference each day.

Doneley Meris, *a psychotherapist and training consultant, is founder and executive director of HIV Arts Network. He was formerly director of bereavement services at the NYC-LGBT Community Center and project administrator of the New York University (NYU) HIV/AIDS Mental Hygiene Project. He is adjunct faculty at CUNY Hunter College School of Social Work and NYU's School of Education and an active member of the Association for Death Education and Counseling (ADEC).*

REFERENCES

Doka, K. J. (2002). *Disenfranchised grief: New directions, challenges, and strategies for practice.* Champaign, IL: Research Press.

Riou, G. (2014). Hospital visitation and medical decision making for same-sex couples. Retrieved from https://www.americanprogress.org/issues/lgbt/news/2014/04/15/88015/hospital-visitation-and-medical-decision-making-for-same-sex-couples/

CHAPTER 8

Military Family Bereavement: Nonverbal Conflict

Jill Harrington-LaMorie

CASE DESCRIPTION

Robert was a single, 30-year-old Army officer living in Manhattan, Kansas, assigned to Fort Riley. He was the second child of Anna, a retired school teacher now living with Robert's older sister, Julia, and her husband, at their home in Fulton, Illinois. Anna had been widowed at age 40, losing her husband to a sudden heart attack.

Robert had had little time for much else other than deploying to war and moving to new duty stations during the last eight years. So, when he found himself at Fort Riley, he started to contemplate how fortunate he had been to survive his combat tours, and how isolated Fort Riley felt to an unmarried soldier. Occasionally, Robert would frequent bars near the base and one night struck up a conversation with Denise, a slightly older woman who had grown up in Manhattan and recently moved back after ending a relationship. They began dating six months before Robert was scheduled to deploy. As his deployment to Afghanistan drew near, the topic of marriage came up.

Thirty days before Robert's deployment, Anna and Julia were shocked and surprised by an exuberant phone call from Robert announcing that he and Denise had gotten married. Anna was skeptical, but ever the optimist, wished the best for her son and looked forward to meeting Denise someday.

During the first month they were married, Robert began to notice changes in their relationship. For example, if they had a conflict, Denise would withdraw and not speak to him, making it difficult to ever resolve a disagreement. Also, she seemed to get aggravated quickly over little things. He tried to remain positive by dismissing these changes as predeployment stress. Now as his wife, Denise wanted control over the finances. To reassure Denise of her importance in his life, he named her the sole beneficiary of his serviceman's group life insurance (SGLI), changing the prior designation of his mother as beneficiary.

On the night before he was to be deployed, Robert was trying to attend to last-minute details and the one thing he did not want to forget was flowers for his new wife. He rushed to the store on that wintery night and never returned home; Robert was killed in a head-on collision.

Each time Robert had deployed, Anna prepared herself for the potential of bad news, but nothing had prepared her for this. The shock was so overwhelming it was hard to feel anything. Also, Robert had never told his mother that he had made Denise his Primary Next of Kin (PNOK) and the Person Assigned to Direct Disposition of Remains (PADD), roles he had previously designated to his mother. Anna may have disagreed with Robert's decision to marry someone he dated briefly, but respected that he defaulted these decisions to his wife. Profoundly devastated, Anna called Denise to help support her and politely offer the family's assistance. She was told by the Casualty Assistance Officer (CAO) that Denise was not taking phone calls, and later was given information from the CAO about when and where the funeral services would occur. Julia and her husband arranged to come with Anna to Ft. Riley for the funeral.

Throughout the planning and at the services, Denise appeared to shut Anna out. She made no mention of Anna or Julia in the church services, barely spoke with either of them, sat them at the end of the first row during the funeral, and put them at the end of the receiving line. After the services, they were neither invited back to Robert's house nor given any of his personal belongings. To add to Anna's devastation, Denise buried Robert at the military cemetery on Fort Riley, even after Anna pleaded with the casualty officer to let Denise know that Robert's explicit wish was to be buried in the family plot in Illinois.

Over the next several months, Anna focused all her energy on trying to make contact with Denise, holding out hope that her silence would lift as her acute grief subsided. By email, voicemail, and regular mail, Anna reached out to Denise with a civil request for some of Robert's personal possessions that were family heirlooms. Her hopes for reciprocal communication kept her focused and distracted. But after six months during which her emails and voicemails went unanswered and her letters returned, she became desperate and hired an attorney who obtained a copy of Robert's probated will. The attorney advised Anna that Denise was designated to handle Robert's personal property, and without a list of named items in his will, Denise had sole discretion to sell, keep, or distribute his belongings.

Upon hearing this from the attorney and realizing that Denise was intentionally shutting her out, Anna fell apart. The more she was shut out, the more difficult it was for her to accept the reality of his death; Anna felt like her Robert had just disappeared. She found herself crying most of the day, having difficulty with simple tasks, and spending the majority of her time staring at pictures of Robert and talking to Julia as if he was still alive. Anna continued to feel angry and bitter about Denise's ungracious behavior, and was stuck in those feelings. When Anna began to reach a point where she felt that her daily pain was intolerable, she asked Julia to help her find a grief counselor.

STATEMENT OF PROBLEM

The choice of whom a service member marries can be a source of great comfort or great distress to a cohesive family of origin. Many service members marry someone they meet while stationed in locations around the world, with whom the family has little or no relationship. As in Robert's case, it is not uncommon for service members to rush relationships and make impulsive decisions out of fear of a transfer to a next duty station, deployment, or death. Additionally, distance can interfere with time needed for both families to bond and develop. Other influences such as language barriers, cultural issues, personality differences, and not gaining family approval of the marriage, can affect interfamily relationships. When a service member dies, much like any nonmilitary family, these dynamics can greatly influence conflict between families, especially when money, benefits, and personal property are involved.

ANALYSIS

Robert's situation—a brief dating relationship with a quick marriage influenced by deployment, followed by an accidental, unanticipated sudden death of a young adult—is not atypical for the military. Nor is it unusual for service members to neglect, either intentionally or accidentally, to discuss with their families who is designated to take care of their affairs after their death. In Anna's case, Robert's neglect to inform his mother that she was no longer in charge of his funeral, burial, or personal effects, caused role confusion as well as the added element of shock in learning that Denise had sole discretion in all these matters. In many cases, family members project their anger onto the designee for their service member's choice or for following military policies. Anna was shocked by the news, however, she was accepting of it. Yet, Denise's disenfranchisement of Anna as a primary family griever had the most significant impact on Anna's loss, impairing her grief and prohibiting adaptation.

The silent treatment, or what researchers call the "demand-withdraw" pattern, is noted to be one of the most toxic patterns in relationship conflict. It happens when one person in a relationship approaches the other with a request and is met with avoidance or silence. In this case, it can be an implicit request for role acknowledgement as a primary griever or an explicit request for personal effects of the deceased. The silent treatment is a known form of maltreatment and is associated with poor negative outcomes, such as depression (Schrodt, Witt, & Messersmith, 2008).

The impact of the silent treatment is underscored in the grief counseling literature. In the case of Anna, Denise's complete disconnection and shutting-out behaviors, some of which were evident in her relationship with Robert, disenfranchised Anna's grief. The primacy of a family at a funeral and acknowledgement of their status in that person's life reaffirms that these survivors experienced a loss and that their subsequent grief needs acknowledgement and support (Doka, 2009). Denise's minimization of Anna's parental status and relationship denied Anna the full opportunity to publicly grieve her son. Anna was neither offered an opportunity to help plan the services, nor given a role in them. The rituals and roles of the funeral and burial services, which normally are helpful in facilitating grief, were not helpful in Anna's case, and may even have been harmful to her mourning as she was intentionally denied an active role.

GOALS OF COUNSELING

Due to the brief and limited nature of their relationship, Anna was not prepared for Denise's personality and coping behaviors. The way in which an individual copes with crisis can influence the grieving process and can contribute to disenfranchisement (Doka, 2009). Denise's passive-aggressive use of the silent treatment and cutting ties with Anna could be seen as an attempt to control her own feelings and the situation in the aftermath of Robert's death.

There are many complex factors in Anna's case that would indicate a higher risk for complicated grief, such as losing an adult child and suffering a sudden, unexpected loss (Beder, 2004). A practitioner could help facilitate the overall goal of grief counseling, which, according to Worden's (2002) task model, is to help the bereaved accept the reality of the loss, adjust to life after loss, and reinvest in one's life through coping with the changes within oneself and the world after loss.

INTERVENTION STRATEGY

Many complex issues must be addressed to help Anna accept the reality of Robert's death, such as acknowledging and validating the silent treatment as maltreatment, processing her feelings around it, and helping her to begin to accept the reality that Denise would most likely never respond to her nor return family heirlooms. Supporting Anna as an enfranchised griever would involve strategies that allow her to publicly mourn her son's death. A local memorial service for friends and family may provide the acknowledgement and support to enfranchise her role, give her the right to grieve, and begin to facilitate an adaptive grief process. Connection to bereaved military family peer support through organizations such as American Gold Star Mothers, Tragedy Assistance Program for Survivors (TAPS), and Army Survivor Outreach Services, would also increase recognition and validation by other bereaved mothers. These organizations also provide opportunities to engage in activities that promote meaning making, such as peer-based retreats, seminars, service projects, and events on Memorial Day and Veterans Day.

CONCLUSIONS AND REFLECTIONS

It is very important to acknowledge that conflict in families does not always present itself as verbal disagreements. Avoidance coping can be a maladaptive strategy to selectively elude stressful situations rather than resolve them, exemplified by the unexpected "wall of silence" encountered by Anna. In working with families, it is critical for the practitioner to understand how this type of behavior can influence the grieving process for the client.

Jill Harrington-LaMorie, DSW, LCSW, is a grief counselor, educator, researcher and consultant. She is the former senior field researcher/

clinician for the National Military Family Bereavement Study and remains a consultant on the project. During an extensive clinical career, she earned her doctorate at The University of Pennsylvania School of Social Policy and Practice. Dr. Harrington-LaMorie served on the board of the Association for Death Education and Counseling (ADEC) from 2012-2015 and remains active as chair of ADEC's Conference Abstract Committee.

REFERENCES

Beder, J. (2004). *Voices of bereavement: A casebook for grief counselors.* New York, NY: Brunner-Routledge.

Doka, K. (2009). Disenfranchised grief. In C. D. Bryant & D. L. Peck (Eds.), *Encyclopedia of death and the human experience* (pp.378-381). Thousand Oaks, CA: Sage Publications.

Schrodt, P., Witt, P. L., & Messersmith, A. S. (2008). A meta-analytical review of family communication patterns and their associations with information processing, behavioral, and psychosocial outcomes. *Communication monographs, 75*(3), 248-269.

Worden, W. (2002). *Grief counseling and grief therapy.* New York, NY: Springer.

CHAPTER 9

Helping Staff Deal with Difficult Deaths

Kenneth J. Doka

CASE DESCRIPTION

Johnny was an 8-year-old boy who had been treated for osteogenic sarcoma in the pediatric unit of a major oncology hospital for the past two years. During this time, Johnny had multiple hospitalizations and was one of the hospital's most frequent patients. He had been there for the diagnosis, amputation of his left arm, and finally chemotherapy and other surgeries, especially after the cancer metastasized to his lungs. The staff on the pediatric unit grew to like Johnny's parents, Andrea and Darren, perceiving them as grateful and non-demanding, yet vulnerable. Most important, over the years, Johnny's personality ingratiated him with the staff. Johnny was a smiling, somewhat mischievous child who responded to his illness with both forbearance and humor. Once, in the waiting room at the hospital, an older woman approached Johnny and Andrea, noting his empty shirt sleeve after his amputation. She exclaimed, "Little boy, I'm so sorry you've lost your arm." Johnny responded by looking surprised and, with mock worry, explained to his mom that he had it before he left.

Johnny loved chocolate-chip cookies. The hospital staff would frequently buy or make cookies for him, so there was always a selection of cookies in his room. Whenever he was hospitalized, his room became an impromptu break room, which further enhanced connections among Johnny, his parents, and staff.

The initial prognosis, even after the first metastases, was guarded but favorable. However, continued metastases in the second lung presaged a poor prognosis. About two years after the initial diagnosis, Johnny's condition deteriorated rapidly following an infection and died. Staff were surprised by the swiftness of his decline and death. During Johnny's final hospitalization, Andrea and Darren rejected extraordinary measures, believing they would unnecessarily prolong his suffering. Some staff had difficulty accepting that decision.

STATEMENT OF PROBLEM

Since Johnny's death, morale on the unit has plummeted. Staff seem reluctant to attach to new patients, and absenteeism has increased. Staff members often tear up when Johnny is mentioned.

ANALYSIS

In their seminal research, Glaser and Strauss (1968) defined *sentimental order* as "the intangible but very real patterning of mood and sentiment that characteristically exists on each ward" (p. 14). In Johnny's case, a number of factors contributed to disrupting the sentimental order. Glaser and Strauss emphasize that staff's ability to predict the timing of a death is a critical factor in maintaining the sentimental order. Not only was there expectation that Johnny would survive the infection, but his death followed an unexpectedly rapid decline.

Other factors contributed to making this case especially difficult. The death of a child is inherently complicated for both parents and medical staff (Rando, 1993). In this case, staff were grieving not only the loss of a special child, Johnny, but the loss of a relationship with his parents. Many of the staff were around the same age as Andrea and Darren, and had children the same age as Johnny, thus easily identified with the parents. The staff also felt a sense of unmet goals. For some, these goals were medical in nature, focused on treating Johnny's infection, which might have prolonged his life or, at least, avoided his rapid and unpredictable decline and death. For some staff, these unmet goals were highly idiosyncratic and personal. For example, one nurse had promised to bake Johnny a batch of chocolate-chip cookies based on a new recipe, but by her next shift, Johnny had already died. All of these unmet goals—medical and personal— are factors identified as intensifying and complicating health professionals' grieving process (Glaser & Strauss, 1968; Papadatou, 2000).

GOALS OF COUNSELING

The hospital must restore the sentimental order in the ward following Johnny's death. Staff need to find ways to process their grief and explore the realities inherent in their work that may be intensifying their grief reactions.

INTERVENTION STRATEGY

The first intervention was a discussion, led by the ethics committee, about Andrea and Darren's decision not to take any extraordinary measures and to allow natural death. As the discussion progressed, though, it became clear that some members of the staff were experiencing unresolved grief and guilt over not being given the opportunity to provide more intensive medical interventions in an attempt to save Johnny. As a result of the initial ethics consult, the hospital decided to do a series of other interventions.

One was unplanned but quite helpful. Johnny's parents wanted to do something to acknowledge the staff's care and support so they offered to host a pizza party between shifts. The party was soothing; it allowed the parents to show appreciation but also gave staff an opportunity to share memories of Johnny and interact with Andrea and Darren again. The event gave them all one final interaction apart from the crisis of dying and Johnny's funeral, which many staff members had attended.

The social worker and chaplain arranged a more formal series of sessions for staff from all shifts to process their grief reactions. This step, both in group and individual settings, provided validation that grief is a natural reaction to loss. This reminder can be critical, as staff sometimes disenfranchise grief reactions to a patient's death as unbecoming to a professional (Doka, 2002; Papadatou, 2000); validating such a loss is helpful (Doka, 2014; Katz & Johnson, 2006; Vachon, 1987).

In these sessions, staff also reviewed self-help strategies they've used to find respite from the intense emotional demands inherent in caring for children with cancer. The sessions also gave them a chance to explore personal philosophies about their roles. Hospital staff often see their primary role as that of curing disease and saving lives. With such a perspective, losing a patient, particularly one who was very special, can be seen as failure and therefore upset the sentimental order. The chaplain and social worker led a discussion utilizing Weisman's notion of *least possible contribution* (1984). This approach encouraged staff to find solace in the little things that they were able to do for the patient rather than focus on what they were unable to do. They found the concept very helpful and began to identify multiple acts of kindness as well as expert medical care that offered comfort and support to Johnny and his family throughout his repeated hospitalizations.

Also during these sessions, the chaplain led a discussion of how each staff member's own spirituality assisted him or her in acknowledging and coping with the unfairness of life. This issue was a major concern when discussing Johnny's death; there was always a sense that the loss of any child was unfair, but Johnny's personality and resilience added a special poignancy to his death, especially with the unexpected nature and speed of his final decline.

The staff had a memorial service every three months commemorating the losses during that quarter but they decided to have a special memorial service for Johnny. It was well attended by staff on all shifts, and included music, reflections, and readings, including one from his favorite book *Where the Wild Things Are*. After the service, there was a reception with milk and chocolate-chip cookies.

CONCLUSIONS AND REFLECTIONS

Some deaths can be difficult for health professionals, especially those considered out-of-order (such as the death of a child or young individual), sudden and unpredictable, or those that do not follow a projected trajectory (Glaser & Strauss, 1968). Such deaths challenge one's assumptions of the world and make one feel an increased vulnerability. In addition, such losses can serve as reminders of past losses, or create fear of future losses (Papadatou, 2000). Johnny's death reminded staff that even children who face illness with optimism are not immune to long-term challenges or death.

Healthcare professionals face other stressors as well. Many have to deal with organizational stress, continually being asked to do more with limited time and resources. These professionals, especially in ICUs, hospices, or palliative care settings, experience cumulative losses. There may be systemic stress arising from the perception, either real or imagined, that patient care has lower priority than financial efficiency. And healthcare professionals will certainly experience personal losses that they may be grieving in addition to the losses they encounter in their work life. Kastenbaum (1988) states that health professionals experience *vicarious grief*; they are likely to have a more realistic concept of the prognosis and grieve the eventual death of the patient, even as the patient and family retain hope.

Another complicating factor is *moral distress*. Jameton (1993) defined moral distress as the inner conflicts experienced by healthcare professionals when they experience personal, professional, spiritual, or ethical dilemmas in the provision of patient care. For example, in Johnny's case, many staff members felt uncomfortable with his parents' decision to allow a natural death.

When deaths are difficult, it is critical both to acknowledge the loss and to offer individual and organizational strategies to cope with that loss. In this case, the hospital did very well in offering support to staff. On an individual level, this means validating and acknowledging that healthcare professionals can grieve a difficult death. Papadatou (2000) stressed that healthcare professionals need to oscillate between experiencing and containing grief. Vachon (1987) emphasized that a critical aspect of lifestyle management was the development and implementation of "respite rules." The staff were given many strategies for stress management.

The sessions also underlined the fact that health professionals need to acknowledge the limitations of their professional role, noting concepts such as Weisman's (1984) *least possible contribution* or Weininger and Kearney's (2011) concept of *exquisite empathy*, meaning a caregiver with self-awareness and effective boundaries, yet who can remain sensitively attuned, warm, and deeply present in caring for patients. Sessions also noted that health professionals were well served by a spiritual/philosophical perspective that allowed them to cope with the continued unfairness of life.

However, Vachon (1987) and Papatadou (2000) noted that effective organizations provide ongoing support for staff. The hospital where Johnny was treated modeled that well. There were formal policies, procedures and programs such as time off to attend funerals, debriefings after difficult deaths, and support groups. The unit offered both education and occasional rituals during which staff could come together to mourn their collective losses.

Some losses are inevitably more difficult than others. Yet, it is still easier when they are borne collectively.

Kenneth J. Doka, PhD, MDiv, is a professor of gerontology at the Graduate School of The College of New Rochelle and senior consultant to Hospice Foundation of America. Dr. Doka serves as editor of HFA's Living with Grief® *book series, its* Journeys *newsletter, and numerous other books and publications. Dr. Doka has served as a panelist on HFA's* Living with Grief® *video programs for 22 years. He is a past president of the Association for Death Education and Counseling (ADEC) and received the Special Contributions Award in the field of Death Education from the Association for Death Education and Counseling. He is a member and past chair of the International Work Group on Death, Dying and Bereavement. In 2006, Dr. Doka was grandfathered in as a mental health counselor under New York's first state licensure of counselors. Dr. Doka is an ordained Lutheran minister.*

REFERENCES

Doka, K. J. (Ed.). (2002). *Disenfranchised grief: New directions, challenges, and strategies for practice.* Champaign, IL: Research Press.

Doka, K. J. (2104). Caring for the carer: The lessons of research. *Progress in Palliative Care, 22* (3), 150-154.

Glaser, B. & Strauss, A. (1968). *Time for dying.* Chicago, IL: Aldine Publishing Company.

Jameton, A. (1993). Dilemmas of moral distress: Moral responsibility and nursing practice. *AWHONNS Clinical Issues in Perinatal & Womens Health Nursing, 4*(4), 542-551.

Kastenbaum, R. (1988). Vicarious grief as an intergenerational phenomenon. *Death Studies, 12,* 447-453.

Katz, R., & Johnson T. (Eds.). (2006). *When professionals weep: Emotional and counter-transference responses in end-of-life care.* New York, NY: Routledge.

Papadatou, D. (2000). A proposed model of health professionals' grieving process. *Omega: Journal of Death and Dying, 41,* 59-77.

Rando, T. A. (1993). *The treatment of complicated mourning.* Champaign, IL: Research Press.

Vachon, M. (1987). *Occupational stress in the care of the critically ill, the dying, and the bereaved.* New York, NY: Hemisphere.

Weininger, R. & Kearney, M. (2011). Revisiting empathic engagement: Countering compassion fatigue with "exquisite empathy." In I. Renzenbrink (Ed.), *Caregiver stress and staff support in illness, dying, and bereavement* (pp. 49-61). Oxford, UK: Oxford University Press.

Weisman, A. (1984). *The coping capacity: On the nature of being mortal.* New York, NY: Human Sciences Press.

PART II

Finding Meaning

CHAPTER 10

Having Their Stories Heard: Dignity Therapy at the End of Life

Lori P. Montross-Thomas and Andrea N. Trejo

CASE DESCRIPTION

Mr. Goldman was fondly, yet candidly described by his hospice team as a "difficult patient." He was a 94-year-old Caucasian male receiving hospice care for colon cancer and congestive heart failure. He lived alone in a 910-square-foot apartment that was built in the 1960s. His apartment was sparsely decorated with the exception of artistic souvenirs from his travels to Africa and China, philosophy and accounting books marked on key pages that were of interest to him, a large television, and an ample supply of Jim Beam whiskey. Mr. Goldman had no children but had been married for 66 years to Willow, whom he described as "the ground of his existence." Unfortunately, Willow had died one year prior to Mr. Goldman's admission onto hospice service, leaving Mr. Goldman alone other than the in-home nursing support he received several days a week.

STATEMENT OF PROBLEM

The team had several reasons to describe Mr. Goldman as "difficult." He was often curt, unwelcoming to visitors, and seemingly embraced his self-described role as a "cranky old man." In many respects he viewed the limited life he could now lead as rather meaningless (e.g., feeling alone after the loss of Willow, being unable to drive due to age-related macular degeneration, and needing ongoing oxygen therapy). He had vehemently declined any mental health counseling or spiritual care services wanting "only the doctors or nurses to step foot in his home." For some reason he agreed to Dignity Therapy, perhaps out of sheer curiosity more than anything else.

Dignity Therapy is a brief, individualized psychotherapy designed to address the emotional needs of adults who are receiving hospice or palliative care (Chochinov, 2002; Chochinov, 2012). During Dignity Therapy, clinicians complete a personal interview with their patients, allowing them to discuss their most important memories, accomplishments, and life roles, as well as any lessons learned in life, and hopes or dreams they may have for their loved ones in the future.

To date, 29 journal articles and one book have been published regarding Dignity Therapy. Overall, Dignity Therapy has been shown to be an acceptable treatment that is well received by patients and families (Fitchett, Emanuel, Handzo, Boyken, & Wilkie, 2015). Patients receiving the treatment have demonstrated an improved sense of dignity and quality of life (Chochinov et al., 2005; Chochinov et al., 2011), with some patients demonstrating reduced depression and anxiety (Juliao, Oliveira, Nunes, Vaz Carneiro, & Barbosa, 2014). Given the benefits of Dignity Therapy, the hospice team made the referral for treatment, and once Mr. Goldman agreed, I became the newly-assigned Dignity Therapist in his case.

When I met Mr. Goldman for the first time, I remember being struck by his inhospitable demeanor and initial greeting of, "You are two minutes late." As we began to discuss the Dignity Therapy process, he was interested in sharing his story, but was hesitant because he had no heirs who could receive the finished document. This was unusual, as most Dignity Therapy patients have one or more specified recipients in mind when sharing their stories, most commonly family members. But in this case, Mr. Goldman expressed satisfaction with the idea that sharing his story would allow others to at least learn from his life experiences in some meaningful way.

As we began his Dignity Therapy interview, Mr. Goldman described a history of family discord due to a mother with mental illness and a verbally abusive father whose "main joy in life was pulling other people down." This home life led to his placement in a large orphanage at the age of nine. He grew up in the orphanage and attended one of the private schools confined within its walls. He remembered being "especially good" in French and science, and being tested with an IQ of 157. Despite his difficult childhood, Mr. Goldman graduated high school at age 16 and attended the University of Chicago, where he built a career as a well-respected court reporter. As he described it, his drive to improve allowed him "to make a name for myself, with quite a reputation for solid technical reporting." He was proud of having worked hard to overcome the adversity in his youth, and for later earning jobs in high profile court cases, ones given only to those reporters with top governmental clearance.

Later in the Dignity Therapy interview Mr. Goldman described his wife, Willow. He spoke warmly of how they met at a picnic when they were in their mid-20s, and laughed quietly when he remembered "somehow ending up sitting back-to-back on the lake rocks…I don't usually get that close so quickly, but there was something special about her!" During this portion of the conversation, I began to see the first signs of this "cranky old man" melting. His tone became softer and more tender, and he provided longer pauses in his speech as he became caught up in the memories. He spoke lovingly of his time spent dancing with Willow on Friday nights. He joked that he had the habit of perspiring, and added, "not just mild perspiration, but sweating *all over*." He said, "It could have been repulsive to somebody else, but Willow never showed any evidence of discomfort. She would simply put her arm around my sweaty neck and gently brush the sweat away." He paused momentarily with this memory, then finished that portion of the interview by saying, "I was truly lucky to have her."

I then asked Mr. Goldman a typical Dignity Therapy question: "When did you feel most alive?" Surprisingly, he replied that he felt most alive when he was writing poetry for Willow. I initially thought, "*This* man wrote poetry?" The possibility of love poetry emanating from him seemed so contrary to his gruff exterior. But he shared how during his courtroom breaks he would construct poems on small sheets of reporter paper (the stenotype machines used paper at that time). He would then put the poems in his pocket and, when he returned home from work each night, he would give them to Willow as he walked through the door.

Learning about his passion for poetry began to spur enlivened conversations between us about his related appreciation for philosophy, and even his larger views regarding the meaning of life. Soon my initial dread about working with this "difficult" patient morphed into delight when I would look at my calendar and see Mr. Goldman's name listed as a planned visit for the day. He was no longer just a "cranky old man" in my eyes, but a multi-faceted human being who had real stories about love, loss, pain, and pride to share. "Perhaps," I thought to myself, "this is what dignity in care is all about."

ANALYSIS

In many respects, Mr. Goldman's stories are representative of Dignity Therapy. We know from qualitative analyses of Dignity Therapy stories that people most often discuss love, families, career roles, and pleasurable hobbies. People also frequently describe times of self-reliance and ways they have overcome challenges, typically through hard work (Hack et al., 2013; Montross, Winters, & Irwin, 2011). Mr. Goldman spoke about all of these. His stories were both "good" and "sad," as is typically the case. In other words, Dignity Therapy does not dismiss the difficult parts of patients' lives, but rather allows for the full, authentic human experience to be shared.

Mr. Goldman's case also demonstrates the potential benefits of asking people, "When did you feel most alive?" As a clinician who has compiled Dignity Therapy documents for over 100 patients, I have seen countless cases of people lighting up when asked this question. Doing so has led to stories about being fearless, loving fully, or simply experiencing life in raw and momentous ways. In that respect, I think this question allows clinicians to see patients at their best. During end-of-life care, asking about levels of current pain and suffering are paramount to providing quality care. Although seeing patients as the robust people they once were, people who at one point *felt very alive*, is also a gift, one that is perhaps even more important to give and receive during people's final days (Montross, Meier, De Cervantes-Monteith, Vashistha, & Irwin, 2013).

GOALS OF COUNSELING

Notably, Dignity Therapy is not meant to produce a full autobiography. The process centers on one personal interview and therefore does not yield a lengthy memoir; most edited stories are approximately 8-12 pages (Montross, Winters, & Irwin, 2011). Instead, the therapy is focused on highlighting the most important aspects of a patient's life as a way to cultivate meaning and a sense of legacy. Furthermore, Dignity Therapy is not meant to emphasize only "happy" memories, but to rather be a genuine snapshot of a person's journey with all its ensuing ups and downs. Most people's stories are a blend of love, joy, and accomplishments, intertwined with personal tragedies as well as regrets or failures (Chochinov, 2012). Mr. Goldman's case demonstrated all these aspects.

INTERVENTION STRATEGY

Dignity Therapy involves hearing and recording important life stories, thereby helping patients remember who they are, or who they were in the past. It encourages people to make meaning of their lives and provides the opportunity for patients to share those thoughts with others. Research has demonstrated that the process leads to an increased sense of dignity and improved quality of life for hospice and palliative care patients. The largest study of Dignity Therapy to date also showed that patients believed the process significantly "changed the way their family sees or appreciates them" (Chochinov et al., 2011). This was true in the case of Mr. Goldman, as the sharing of his story granted the opportunity for him "to be fully seen," at least by me as his clinician and perhaps by others who may have the fortunate chance to read his story in the future.

CONCLUSIONS AND REFLECTIONS

As Mr. Goldman and I completed his Dignity Therapy story edits and were finalizing the legacy document, he decided to include one of his favorite William Butler Yeats poems, *The Coming of Wisdom with Time*. He cited the poem extemporaneously during our session as follows:

> During all the lying days of my youth,
> I spread my leaves in the sun,
> Now that my life is nearly done,
> I may wither into the truth.

When placing the final layout for print, I realized that the quote he provided was technically inaccurate and asked him if he wanted me to change it to the exact words written by Yeats. He thought about it pensively, openly debating between paying respects to one of his favorite poets, yet enjoying how his version of the poem read as well. Ultimately, he asked me to leave it as shown above and we placed it as the preface in his final Dignity Therapy story. "Besides," he said, "I like my version better."

Lori P. Montross-Thomas, PhD, is a licensed psychologist and assistant professor in the Department of Family Medicine and Public Health at the University of California, San Diego (UCSD). Dr. Montross-Thomas is one of 95 Americans formally trained in Dignity Therapy by Dr. Harvey M. Chochinov, the therapy's originator. Over the past 15 years, Dr. Montross-Thomas has been engaged in research focused on dignity, hospice care, positive psychology, resilience, and successful aging. She has received funding for her research from the American Cancer Society (ACS), the Clinical and Translational Research Institute (CTRI), the International Alzheimer's Association, the National Alliance for Research on Schizophrenia and Depression (NARSAD), and the MAPI Research Trust.

Andrea N. Trejo *is studying psychology at the University of California, San Diego. She has served as a research assistant in the UCSD Department of Family Medicine and Public Health for the past two years. In this role, she helps coordinate the current 5-year randomized controlled trial of Dignity Therapy funded by the American Cancer Society and supervised by Dr. Montross-Thomas as the Principal Investigator. She previously conducted a study on the effects of pediatric cancer on sibling relationship quality, for which she was awarded a scholarship from SuperSibs!, a non-profit organization that provides support for pediatric cancer patients and their siblings.*

References

Chochinov, H. M. (2002). Dignity-conserving care—a new model for palliative care: Helping the patient feel valued. *Journal of the American Medical Association, 287*(17), 2253-2260.

Chochinov, H. M. (2012). *Dignity Therapy: Final words for final days.* New York, NY: Oxford University Press.

Chochinov, H. M., Hack, T., Hassard, T., Kristjanson, L. J., McClement, S., & Harlos, M. (2005). Dignity Therapy: A novel psychotherapeutic intervention for patients near the end of life. *Journal of Clinical Oncology, 23,* 5520-5525.

Chochinov, H. M., Kristjanson, L. J., Breitbart, W., McClement, S., Hack, T. F., Hassard, T., & Harlos, M. (2011). Effect of dignity therapy on distress and end-of-life experience in terminally ill patients: A randomised controlled trial. *The Lancet Oncology, 12*(8), 753-762.

Fitchett, G., Emanuel, L., Handzo, G., Boyken L., & Wilkie, D. J. (2015). Care of the human spirit and the role of dignity therapy: A systematic review of dignity therapy research. *BMC Palliative Care, 14*(8), 1-12.

Hack, T. F., McClement, S. E., Chochinov, H. M., Cann, B. J., Hassard, T. H., Kristjanson, L. J., & Harlos, M. (2013). Learning from dying patients during their final days: Life reflections gleaned from dignity therapy. *Palliative Medicine, 24*(7), 715-723.

Juliao, M., Oliveira, F., Nunes, B., Vaz Carneiro, A., & Barbosa, A. (2014). Efficacy of dignity therapy on depression and anxiety in Portuguese terminally ill patients: A phase II randomized controlled trial. *Journal of Palliative Medicine, 17*(6), 688-695.

McClement, S., Chochinov, H. M., Hack, T., Hassard, T., Kristjanson, L. J., and Harlos, M. (2007). Dignity therapy: Family member perspectives. *Journal of Palliative Medicine, 10*(5), 1076-1082.

Montross, L. P., Meier, E. A., De Cervantes-Monteith, K., Vashistha, V., & Irwin, S. A. (2013). Hospice staff perspectives on Dignity Therapy. *Journal of Palliative Medicine, 16*(9), 1118-1120.

Montross, L., Winters, K. D., and Irwin, S. A. (2011). Dignity therapy implementation in a community-based hospice setting. *Journal of Palliative Medicine, 14* (6), 729-734.

Resilience and Posttraumatic Growth

Some people have a comparatively limited reaction to loss. Part of this resilience is due to situational factors. Resilient grievers had fewer losses or other stresses and the death was not sudden so there was a chance to say goodbye. Yet resilient grievers also shared personal characteristics. They had an intrinsic spirituality and good psychological health where loss was seen as a challenge. They were generally optimistic and shared a belief that even in the worst situations, they could learn and grow. Resilient grievers focused on positive memories (Bonanno, 2009; Doka, 2016).

Are resilient people more likely to experience posttraumatic growth? If resilience is defined as the ability to transform negative experiences, certainly yes. But Calhoun and Tedeschi's (2006) sense of posttraumatic growth suggests resilient people are less likely to experience significant personal growth since they weather the trauma well. Both the resilient griever and someone who experiences posttraumatic growth have in common the ability to create something positive out of a negative experience. In resilience, this occurs almost naturally, while the posttraumatic growth model stresses that growth results from the struggle. Calhoun and Tedeschi suggest there is a curvilinear relationship, as some resilience is needed in order to grow, but if the person is highly resilient, the loss may not engender further growth.

—*Kenneth J. Doka*

REFERENCES

Bonanno, G. (2009). *The other side of sadness: What the new science of bereavement tells us about life after loss.* New York, NY: Basic Books.

Doka, K. J. (2016). *Grief is a journey: Finding your path through loss.* New York: Atria Books.

Calhoun, L. G., & Tedeschi, R. G. (Eds.) (2006). *Handbook of posttraumatic growth: Research and practice.* Mahwah, NJ: Lawrence Erlbaum Associates.

CHAPTER 11

Understanding the Grief Responses of Military Children

Donna Burns Stewart

D
evelopmental psychologists, bereavement specialists, and clinicians concur that conceptualizations of and responses to loss are reflective of the griever's level of cognitive and socioemotional development (e.g., Burns, 2010; Kaplow, Layne, Saltzman, Cozza, & Pynoos, 2013; Swank & Robinson, 2009). Although military children share the same developmental characteristics as other bereaved children, there are elements unique to this population of grievers (e.g., Campagna, Saari, & Harrington-LaMorie, 2014; Kaplow et al., 2013; Swank & Robinson, 2009). A brief overview of the sequence of events from deployment through post-death encapsulates some of the grieveable concerns of military children and adolescents that set them apart from the civilian population of same-age grievers. The illustrative case that follows, drawn from the author's professional experiences, depicts the ways developmental trajectories affect how children and adolescents grieve. Each child's grief path and behavioral responses will be viewed from a cognitive and socioemotional developmental lens with a focus on the death of a military parent. Recommendations, strategies, and resources that support bereaved military children will be provided.

For many military children, deployment of a parent may result in separation anxiety. Missing and worrying about the parent's safety may manifest itself in the form of ambiguous loss, whereby the family is anxious and concerned because their loved one, although psychologically present, is not physically present (e.g., Boss, 2009; Kaplow et al., 2013; National Child Traumatic Stress

Network [NCTSN], 2008; Swank & Robinson, 2009). Concomitant with ambiguous loss is a sense of disenfranchisement that military children may feel when among their civilian friends and peers. Disenfranchisement may be experienced throughout parental deployment. Disenfranchised children may feel isolated because their sadness and loss over parental absence may not be understood, recognized, or supported by their nonmilitary peers (e.g., Burns, 2010; Doka, 2002).

When a United States service member is killed, the military is immediately involved. Every branch of the service has a Casualty Assistance Representative assigned to the family who plays an integral role in assuring that the immediate needs of the family are met. In addition to notifying the family of the death, the representative assists with the preparation and filing of documents, provides support and resources, and remains with the family until their services are no longer required (*Casualty Assistance Officer*, n.d.). Throughout this entire time the family is surrounded by compassionate and knowledgeable personnel who help them navigate this critical process.

The period following the burial and ceremonies often brings about dramatic changes for those military families who have lived in a close-knit military community. Making the transition from a military to a civilian community brings about numerous challenges, particularly for children. The entire constellation of the child's world changes when a move to a different and unfamiliar community takes place. The previous network of neighbors, friends, schools, and classmates is upended. This can be a very distressing time as children must now adapt to a way of life that is unfamiliar to them (e.g., Campagna et al., 2014; Kaplow et al., 2013; NCTSN, 2008; Swank & Robinson, 2009).

CASE DESCRIPTION

It has been almost three months since the father of Tyler, Amber, and Dillon, who was a sergeant in the Army, was killed overseas. The first few days and weeks were filled with a blur of activities, including gatherings of family and friends, a military funeral, pastoral care, community support, and military tributes. Being encircled by a continuous flow of caring others provided much needed comfort to the three children, but soon the reality and pain of their devastating loss began to emerge once the revolving door of activities slowed. As the weeks following their father's death unfolded, their mother, coping with her own grief while attempting to maintain a healthy home for the children, began to notice changes in their behaviors.

Tyler, 15, was very close to his father. They loved playing football in the yard and watching college games together. He was proud of his dad's military service and aspired to be like him; he was enrolled in his school's Junior Reserve Officer Training Corps (JROTC).

Amber, 11, was the proverbial "Daddy's girl." He was her hero and she wrote to him every day when he was deployed. She ended each letter with, "I love you, Daddy," embellished with hearts and flowers. She and her brothers would Skype with their father whenever they could.

Dillon, 6, was fascinated by his "soldier" dad. Although his father was deployed throughout much of Dillon's young life, when he was home Dillon liked to curl up on his lap to be read his favorite stories about superheroes.

STATEMENT OF PROBLEM

Each of the children grieved the loss differently. Tyler became sullen and angry and skipped his JROTC classes. Although unprovoked, he would start fights with other kids. Amber began to spend more time in her room. She cried a lot, didn't complete her homework assignments, and performed poorly in school. Dillon was confused and started to have nightmares. Each child, experiencing the same loss, responded in ways reflective of his or her developmental stage.

ANALYSIS

Tyler's reactions exemplify the intrinsic connection between cognitive and socioemotional development. Characteristics of the cognitive processes of mid-adolescence include an increased ability to think logically and abstractly; this contributes to a more mature understanding of the causality of death. Simultaneously, a hallmark of this period is increased independence as the teen grapples with issues of personal identity (Burns, 2010). Tyler's father, as noted, was a role model to his son; Tyler wanted to follow in his footsteps. Tyler's grief responses manifested themselves in the form of anger, defiance, and aggression. His impulsive and risk-taking behaviors, although seeming to contradict the love and admiration he had for his father, actually revealed the frustration, hurt, and outrage he had over losing one of the most important people in his life.

Amber, the self-proclaimed "Daddy's girl," became socially isolated and began to exhibit signs of anxiety. Her grades began to drop and she showed little interest in doing things that she previously enjoyed. Her grief reactions in response to the death of her beloved father are consistent with children in early adolescence. Cognitive and socioemotional responses to loss during this developmental period are mediated by the degree of attachment or connectedness the child has to the deceased loved one. Additionally, both gender and hormonal changes associated with puberty may also have contributed to Amber's behaviors, further exacerbating the pain of her loss (Burns, 2010; Davila, 2008).

Although Dillon, the youngest, understood that his father died, he could not fully grasp the fact that he would never return. He questioned why his dad couldn't come back, like his superheroes did. He became curious and asked many questions and struggled with nightmares. These reactions are common in early childhood and reflect developing, yet immature, cognitive and socioemotional development. Dillon's magical thinking, a belief that his thoughts and wishes could make things happen, contributed in part to understanding and making sense of the circumstances of his father's death (Burns, 2010).

GOALS OF COUNSELING

Communicating with bereaved military children is not as daunting as it may seem. There are some simple, yet effective techniques that can be incorporated to help children understand and manage their grieving process (Burns, 2013). These techniques include:

- having an awareness of the circumstances of the loss and focusing on the needs of the child or adolescent;
- understanding how cognitive, social, and emotional development affect responses to loss;
- listening, observing, and taking cues from the child—a quiet presence can be very comforting;
- adopting a nonjudgmental, respectful, and mindful approach to seeing how the loss is being perceived and processed; and
- providing opportunities for grief to be expressed through a variety of activities.

INTERVENTION STRATEGY

The recommendations and strategies provided, while beneficial to most grieving children, are adapted to focus on the unique needs of bereaved military children. These include effective communication techniques, rituals, and helpful resources.

One developmentally-appropriate activity that may provide bereaved children and teens with a sense of control and a measure of comfort involves the creation of and participation in rituals (Burns, 2010; Doka, 2000; Swank & Robinson, 2009). Rituals are symbolic activities or ceremonies that hold special meaning for the person or group engaging in them and may facilitate the grief and loss process (Burns, 2010; Swank & Robinson, 2009). According to Doka (2000), a ritual "provides a meaningful, structured activity that allows individuals space, time, and support to recognize, respond to, and absorb a significant change" (pp. 154-155). The planning of and participation in rituals by children and teens facilitates healthy grieving and, according to Doka (2000), presents opportunities to express grief in nonverbal ways. Rituals can be thought of as "tangibles." Through these activities, grievers are encouraged to incorporate healing practices in ways that are personally meaningful. Children and teens are amazingly sensitive and adept at creating poignant rituals. Keep in mind that the rituals they create will be largely reflective of their level of cognitive and socioemotional development (Burns, 2010; Doka, 2000). To help guide bereaved military children in the creating, planning, and implementing of their ideas, consider the following (Burns, 2010): Begin by asking the children what they would like to do; brainstorm ideas with them if they are hesitant or appear unsure; and allow them choices among the ideas that have been generated.

Rituals and other tangible activities come in a variety of forms and may be engaged in privately or publicly. Some may be implemented right away, while others may require permission and planning (Burns, 2010). Some suggested ideas for grieving military children include art projects, writing letters or poetry, a balloon launch, planting a tree, or participation in a memorial sporting event. A facilitator guides this process, and the children should be given the choice as to how they would like to express their feelings and commemorate the loss (Burns, 2010).

It is important to note that in some cases the approaches addressed here may not be sufficient and counseling may be necessary. There are, however, reliable resources that support grieving military families and provide a variety of services to help children. Organizations and support groups familiar with military loss offer valuable programs to the military community and can direct families to additional interventions and counseling services, should they be required (*Bereavement and Grief*, n.d.; NCTSN, 2008).

Conclusions and Reflections

Grief responses vary from person to person depending upon the context and nature of the loss. The death of a parent evokes myriad grief responses and navigating grief can be a confusing and frightening experience for children and adolescents. The age and developmental status of the child or adolescent is a significant factor in understanding the grief reactions. Additionally, the relationship the child had with the parent is noteworthy. The death of a military parent may be further complicated because of the uniqueness of military life. Children of a military parent who has been killed often experience a sense of disenfranchisement and loss prior to the death, during the parent's deployment. The notification of death, beginning with the appearance of uniformed service members at the door, initiates a sequence of events which includes funeral and burial arrangements, graveside services, and military tributes. After the activities have subsided, the family, with the help of the Casualty Assistance Representative, must file required documents and, in many cases, make new living arrangements. These post-death events activate another constellation of grieveable issues that are nonfinite. Moving from a military installation or community into a civilian locality can be difficult for children as they adapt to a new lifestyle. The grief issues specific to military children speak to the need for compassionate understanding and stable, reliable resources that support our military families.

Donna Burns Stewart, PhD, holds a doctorate in educational psychology and is an educator, author, and consultant. She is a former professor in the Department of Educational and School Psychology at the College of Saint Rose in Albany, New York. She taught courses in developmental psychology and specializes in issues of grief and loss. She has presented papers on various aspects of grief and loss and has created a conceptual framework that examines the multi-faceted nature of responses to loss. Dr. Burns Stewart coordinates and oversees the children's program for the annual New York State Police Survivor's Tribute Weekend and provides educational training and support to bereaved military families. Dr. Burns Stewart is a member of the Association for Death Education and Counseling (ADEC) and received training in advanced bereavement facilitation from the American Academy of Bereavement (AAB). She is the author of numerous works, including When kids are grieving: Addressing grief and loss in school *(Corwin Press, 2010).*

Recommended resources for military families:
Military OneSource http://www.militaryonesource.com

National Child Traumatic Stress Network (NCTSN) http://www.nctsn.org

National Military Family Association (NMFA) http://www.nmfa.org

Tragedy Assistance Program for Survivors (TAPS) http://www.taps.org/youth/

REFERENCES

Bereavement and grief: Information for military families and communities. (n.d.). Retrieved from http://www.mentalhealthamerica.net/conditions/bereavement-and-grief-information-military-families-and-communities

Boss, P. (2009). *Loss, trauma, and resilience.* New York, NY: W.W. Norton.

Burns, D. M. (2010). *When kids are grieving: Addressing grief and loss in school.* Thousand Oaks, CA: Corwin Press.

Burns, D. M. (2013, August). *The landscape of grief: How loss affects patients, families, and you.* Schwartz Center Grand Rounds presentation, Stratton Veteran's Administration Medical Center, Albany, NY.

Campagna, H. R., Saari, T., & Harrington-LaMorie, J. (2014). Adolescent grief: The death of a U.S. service member. In K. J. Doka & A. S. Tucci (Eds.), *Living with grief: Helping adolescents cope with loss* (pp. 183-199). Washington, DC: Hospice Foundation of America.

Casualty Assistance Officer. (n.d.). Retrieved from http://www.military.com/benefits/survivor-benefits/casualty-assistance-officer.html

Davila, J. (2008). Depressive symptoms and adolescent romance: Theory, research, and implications. *Child Development Perspectives, 2,* 26-31.

Doka, K. J. (2000). Using rituals with children and adolescents. In K. J. Doka, (Ed.), *Living with grief: Children, adolescents, and loss* (pp. 153-160). Washington, DC: Hospice Foundation of America.

Doka, K. J. (2002). *Disenfranchised grief: New directions, challenges, and strategies for practice.* Champaign, IL: Research Press.

Kaplow, J. B., Layne, C. M., Saltzman, W. R., Cozza, S. J., & Pynoos, R. S. (2013). Using multidimensional grief theory to explore the effects of deployment, reintegration, and death on military youth and families. *Psychology Review, 16*, 322-340. doi: 10.1007/s10567-013-0143-1

National Child Traumatic Stress Network, (2008). *Traumatic grief in military children: Information for families.* Los Angeles, CA & Durham, NC: National Center for Child Traumatic Stress.

Swank, J. M. & Robinson, E. H. M. (2009, March). *Addressing grief and loss issues with children and adolescents of military families.* Paper based on a program presented at the American Counseling Association Annual Conference and Exposition, Charlotte, NC.

CHAPTER 12

Posttraumatic Growth: Forging New Meaning and Purpose after Loss

Bret A. Moore

CASE DESCRIPTION

Marie is a 55-year-old woman who lives in a small town in central Texas. Her three adult children, ages 28, 25, and 22, are self-sufficient and live on their own. Marie has taught English at the local high school for 26 years, and even though she is able to retire now, she plans to teach for another year or two. Marie is often described as a very dedicated and hard-working teacher; she is usually the first person to arrive at school and the last one to leave. In addition to bringing work home with her nightly, she volunteers to tutor students three evenings a week and on Saturdays. She has few friends and the only social interaction she has outside of school is attendance at church on most Sunday mornings. Her social relationships at work and church would be considered superficial at best.

Approximately eight months ago, John, Marie's husband of 37 years, died of a heart attack. John's death was sudden and unexpected. If you were to ask people who knew John to describe him, they would likely say he was vibrant, energetic, and athletic. Until his death, John coached basketball at the same high school where Marie teaches.

John and Marie were considered a happy couple by most outside observers. Marie and John described their marriage as strong and supportive. Like most couples, they argued about such things as money, work, and the children, but overall they were happy together. They even called each other "best friends."

STATEMENT OF PROBLEM

Marie sought counseling about three months after John's death. During the intake process, she described herself as lonely and lost. She was relatively free of anxiety and sleep disturbances but she reported a number of depressive symptoms. Most days she felt sad and would become tearful for no particular reason. She lost her appetite; although she tried to eat, she had lost 20 pounds over the preceding months. Although Marie denied any thoughts of wanting to die, she did acknowledge going to bed some nights wishing she wouldn't wake up.

The most notable change in Marie, however, was her withdrawal from family and the few people she would spend time with at school and church. Although she maintained her focus and unwavering work ethic at school, she stopped tutoring students. She stopped calling her own children, a stark change, as she called them at least once a week before John's death. One of the teachers at her school and a few members of her church invited her to go for lunch or dinner on several occasions, but Marie politely declined each offer.

The question, "If you could change one thing about your situation, what would it be?" is a standard part of the intake process and was asked of Marie. Without hesitation Marie replied, "I want my best friend back. I want to stop being so lonely." Marie was hesitant about attending counseling; she had only agreed to the initial appointment as a promise to her children. At the end of the intake she agreed to meet weekly.

ANALYSIS

For Marie, the sudden and unexpected loss of John was traumatic, not in the traditional clinical use of the term that is often associated with conditions like posttraumatic stress disorder, but as a severe emotional shock that altered her life course. Marie was very content with her life prior to John's death. She found meaning and purpose in her work, took pride in knowing that she raised three healthy and happy children, and believed she was fortunate to have a husband who understood her and whom she considered a friend.

Marie knew she was depressed and understood that this was an expected and normal response after such a terrible event. What Marie didn't expect was how lonely she felt and how withdrawn she became. Even though she interacted with at least a dozen teachers at her school and participated in a Bible study group at her church, she was surprised she could not find support and comfort in those around her.

At some level, neither fully understood nor articulated, Marie knew that there was a void in her life that had existed prior to John's death. She began to realize that the reason she couldn't find support from those around her is that her connections with those she worked and attended church with were not deep. They were more acquaintances than friends.

GOALS OF COUNSELING

The initial goal of counseling was to alleviate Marie's depression and help her manage her emotional distress. A secondary goal that evolved during therapy was to help her better understand the void she'd already identified, which she believed was related to a lack of connectedness with others. This goal fit within the context of facilitating posttraumatic growth for Marie, which is the experience of growth in one or more of the following areas: personal strength, relating to others, new possibilities in life, appreciation of life, and spirituality (Brunet, McDonough, Hadd, Crocker, & Sabiston, 2010; Taku, Cann, Calhoun, & Tedeschi, 2008).

INTERVENTION STRATEGY

Over several weeks, Marie's depression lifted to a significant degree. Through a course of cognitive therapy, she was able to identify multiple automatic and self-defeating thoughts which fueled her sadness. For example, two pervasive automatic thoughts were: "I will never feel better," and "I'm destined to suffer." Marie also learned various breathing and imagery techniques which helped her manage unpredictable periods in which she would become flooded and overwhelmed with sadness and grief. These episodes would overtake her mind and body and when they happened she could only curl up into a ball and cry. Learning to focus on her breathing and engaging in imagery helped her to deflect and eventually avoid these highly distressing episodes. This approach is a key step in helping people overcome the grief associated with trauma and support the process of growth (Calhoun & Tedeschi, 2013).

Although Marie's depression improved, her sense of emptiness and loneliness remained. As therapy continued, it became evident that a core belief of Marie's had been challenged after John's death: that she only needed John to help her feel whole; only he could provide the emotional support and friendship she needed. Marie was consumed with thoughts that related to the idea that only John could meet her emotional needs. Using previous cognitive techniques that helped reduce her depression, Marie's therapist helped her challenge these thoughts and explore other possibilities with regard to meeting her emotional needs.

As Marie's sense of emptiness lessened, she and her therapist explored the impact John's death had on her views about the concept of friends. Specifically, what was her role and the role of others in friendships? What constitutes a friendship versus an acquaintance? And how does one develop and nurture friendships?

Marie and her therapist also discussed the concept of how there can be growth after loss, which is the greatest paradox of posttraumatic growth. Together they explored the possibility of Marie writing a new story of her life. Instead of staying on her current course in which she would live her life as if only John could meet her emotional needs, she explored other possibilities. She was asked to write a story of her life assuming nothing would change and that she'd stay on the same course she was currently on. She was then asked to write a new posttrauma story of her life but to keep in mind that she is in control of how things turn out. She was asked to identify how she would like things to be different and in what ways would she be stronger, wiser, or experience a greater connectedness to others. Over several weeks Marie and her therapist discussed these two narratives in detail.

Over the next few months, Marie noticed that she enjoyed talking more with the teachers at her school and other women in her Bible study group. She also noticed that when someone would ask her how she was doing, she would actually tell them in some detail, as opposed to her past standard response, "I'm fine." She developed significant emotional connections to several people. Towards the end of therapy, she formed a close bond with a woman named Allison from her school; Allison had also experienced the sudden death of her husband, several years before. Allison and Marie became very close. Marie terminated therapy free from depression and with a newfound sense of connectedness to others. She had a new purpose in her life, which is to make as many deep emotional connections as possible. This became her new story.

CONCLUSIONS AND REFLECTIONS

Posttraumatic growth is neither guaranteed nor predictable in its pattern. Furthermore, it may not be as profound or "complete" as Marie's experience. It is, however, fairly common. Some degree of growth after trauma has been estimated to occur in 30% to 90% of people (Calhoun & Tedeschi, 2006). It is important to keep in mind that if growth is to occur it will occur over time and generally only after the individual is able to manage the intense grief, sadness, fear, and loss that often follows trauma. Introducing the idea of growth after trauma early on can be appropriate and therapeutic, but "pushing" growth onto the client prematurely will weaken the relationship and hamper progress.

Bret A. Moore, PsyD, ABPP, is a prescribing psychologist and board-certified clinical psychologist in San Antonio, Texas. He is a former active duty Army psychologist and two-tour veteran of Iraq. He is the author and editor of 13 books, including Treating PTSD in Military Personnel: A Clinical Handbook; Wheels Down: Adjusting to Life after Deployment; *and* Taking Control of Anxiety: Small Steps for Overcoming Worry, Stress, and Fear. *Dr. Moore is a Fellow of the American Psychological Association (APA) and recipient of the Arthur W. Melton Award for Early Career Achievement in Military Psychology from Division 19, and the Early Career Achievement Award in Public Service Psychology from Division 18, of APA. His views on clinical and military psychology have been quoted in* USA Today, The New York Times, *and* The Boston Globe, *and on CNN and Fox News. He has appeared on NPR, the BBC, and CBC.*

REFERENCES

Brunet, J., McDonough, M. H., Hadd, V., Crocker, P. E., & Sabiston, C. M. (2010). The Posttraumatic Growth Inventory: An examination of the factor structure and invariance among breast cancer survivors. *Psycho-Oncology, 19*(8), 830-838.

Calhoun, L. G. & Tedeschi, R. G. (2013). *Posttraumatic growth in clinical practice.* New York, NY: Routledge.

Calhoun, L. G. & Tedeschi, R. G. (Eds.). (2006) *Handbook of posttraumatic growth: Research and practice.* Mahwah, NJ: Lawrence Erlbaum Associates.

Taku, K., Cann, A., Calhoun, L. G., & Tedeschi, R. G. (2008). The factor structure of the Posttraumatic Growth Inventory: A comparison of five models using confirmatory factor analysis. *Journal of Traumatic Stress, 21*(2), 158-164.

Growth in Grief

The idea that struggling with illness and loss can empower personal growth seems insensitive, yet, as Calhoun and Tedeschi (2006) note, such events challenge an individual's assumptions of the world and in that challenge, growth is possible. Such growth can be manifested in a number of different areas.

- *Greater appreciation of life, relationships, and a reorienting of priorities* When we lose someone we love, we gain a keener understanding of loss. For some, that may mean cherishing remaining ties and recognizing that time is limited. Ties with family and friends can become closer and we may become more conscious of priorities.

- *Deepened spirituality and existential awareness* Illness and loss can challenge beliefs. These experiences may cause some to lose their faith; they may cause others to ponder questions on a much deeper level. Spirituality arising from the struggle is far more resilient and can encompass questions of pain and suffering.

- *Changes in lifestyle* The illness or death of a loved one can make some review their own lifestyle and health practices. Faced with morbidity and mortality, individuals may decide to give up unhealthy practices such as smoking, or begin a renewed health ritual.

- *Growth in skills* An individual dealing with another's illness or death may be forced to take on new roles and master new tasks and duties. In doing so, the person may discover talents, skills, or abilities heretofore unacknowledged.

- *Growth in character* Individuals may also gain a stronger sense of self and self-esteem; they may be surprised by their own strength, acknowledging aspects of character previously unrecognized. Confidence in one's own ability to cope can grow exponentially.

Counselors can take steps to enhance growth in clients.

- *Use empowering language* Words such as "courage" or "challenge" empower clients. Avoid victim language; for example, use "Surviving Spouses" rather than calling it a "Widow's Group."

- *Remember that small choices empower bigger ones* Constantly challenge clients with the language of choice (i.e., *Where will you choose to spend the holidays?*). This approach assists clients in seeing themselves as active, rather than passive victims of loss.

- *Discuss both positive and negative adaptions* As we counsel individuals, remember that they learn as much, if not more, by analyzing what succeeded as well as what did not.

- *Review strategies that have worked in the client's past* Such review reminds clients that they survived past crises.

- *Focus on personal strengths and positive connections* This reinforces strengths and reminds clients that they do not have to cope with their loss alone.

- *Reflect on the ways the loss has changed them* This allows clients to recognize and acknowledge positive adaptations as they occur.

- *Concentrate on the future* Have clients envision their hopes for the future and assist them in planning ways to achieve that future.

—Kenneth J. Doka

REFERENCES

Calhoun, L. G. & Tedeschi, R. G. (Eds.) (2006). *Handbook of posttraumatic growth: Research and practice*. Mahwah, NJ: Lawrence Erlbaum Associates.

CHAPTER 13

What a year it's been

Coping after Suicide

Joanne L. Harpel

Case Description

Samantha, a woman in her early 40s, first contacted me by email at the suggestion of her grief counselor, with whom she'd been working following the suicide of her 41-year-old husband Jake two years earlier. Samantha described Jake's death as having been the culmination of his longstanding depression exacerbated by significant business stresses, obsessive-compulsive disorder (OCD), and a perfectionist nature borne of growing up in a toxic family with no tolerance for weakness or vulnerability. Though supportive of others with mental health issues, he "could not or would not find help himself" (personal communication, November 19, 2014).

Samantha, now a single mother with two adolescent sons, wrote of how she was "slowly picking up the pieces" including moving with her boys from her small Midwestern hometown now filled with "sadness, grief, and stigma," to a waterfront community on the East Coast.

In an introductory phone conversation, she and I explored whether my services would be a good fit for her. As a professional suicide bereavement and postvention advisor, I've worked with hundreds of individuals, families, schools, workplaces, and communities coping with the aftermath of suicide. I am also the former longtime Senior Director for Public Affairs and Postvention for the largest nonprofit suicide prevention organization in the world and the survivor of my own brother's suicide more than 20 years ago. But I am not a licensed clinician. So it was important to both of us that she have a clear sense of how our work together could help her address the suicide-specific aspects of her loss.

STATEMENT OF PROBLEM

Samantha felt she "lost herself for the past two years" and said she "stopped working and volunteering, and after the fog lifted could only focus on making sure my boys had the help, care and support they needed to grieve and start to heal." She continued, "I now feel stuck. I'm tired of reacting to my life. It is time for me to be proactive again [and] discover who I am." She yearned to somehow be Samantha again, not merely The Widow Whose Husband Had Killed Himself.

ANALYSIS

She craved to reestablish herself personally and professionally but was "hiding and fearful" of the judgment and recrimination she'd received, perceived, and now anticipated. And she questioned whether she could, as she put it, summon the "strength and courage to take even simple steps to put myself out there again."

GOALS OF COUNSELING

Samantha had come to define herself as a "suicide widow." She was angry at Jake for having left her and their boys; enraged at the many people whom she'd counted on for support but who instead had criticized and judged her, including her in-laws; fearful of the future; and unsure of her own ability to craft a new life for herself in the face of her life-altering and traumatic loss.

In anticipation of our first session, I encouraged Samantha to purchase a beautiful journal, select a pen that felt especially comfortable in her hand, and spend at least 15 minutes writing continuously in response to the following prompt: "Write a letter to yourself. Date it one year from today, and begin with, *What a year it's been . . .*" I assured her that it would be entirely her decision whether to share any of what she'd written with me when we met.

INTERVENTION STRATEGY

I often use this exercise with new clients (provided they are not newly, acutely bereaved) because writing about the upcoming year retrospectively can create an opening to experience the sense of hopefulness that comes from having made progress. Samantha later described it this way: "On our first phone call, you suggested I write my *What a year it's been* journal entry. You gave me the courage to think about myself in the future and be honest with what I wanted and could achieve and become. An amazing experience" (personal communication, October 27, 2015).

Self-reflection (including through journaling exercises) is one of several approaches to coping after suicide that I typically explore with clients. Other approaches include:

- connection (including with other survivors of suicide loss, both individually and as part of a new community);
- education (including psychoeducation about mental illness, suicide, and the common themes of suicide bereavement); and
- action (identifying and taking specific steps to help integrate the loss and facilitate meaning making).

In our first session together, I incorporated some limited self-disclosure about my personal path of coping after suicide, which I've found can often begin to normalize their own experience and help put it into context and perspective. As Samantha subsequently said, "You were the first person who was honest and open about your loss by suicide. The stories and feelings you shared validated my feelings. I knew I wasn't crazy, which at times I believed."

Later, I connected Samantha with Deborah, whose situation was very similar. Her husband had killed himself several years before and she was raising young teenagers, while her in-laws aggressively blamed her for her husband's death. Like Samantha, she, too, was seeking to redefine herself and recreate her life, and had also decided it was healthiest to relocate. Their conversation helped relieve Samantha of some of the intense guilt she'd felt about needing to seek geographic and emotional distance from her in-laws, relief she described as a "most beautiful guilt." It also provided an opportunity for the healing laughter and admittedly dark humor that becomes uniquely possible when survivors of suicide loss feel free to speak candidly.

The educational element in Samantha's case included exploring many of the common features of surviving suicide loss (Baugher & Jordan, 2002) and those of spouse-survivors in particular (Fine, 1997). I also introduced her to the concept of posttraumatic growth and the work of Richard Tedeschi and Lawrence Calhoun (www.ptgi.uncc. edu) and Melinda Moore (www.posttraumaticgrowth.com), as well as a self-help book by Tara Mohr entitled, *Playing Big: Find Your Voice, Your Mission, Your Message* (2014), which Samantha later described as having "provided [her] the biggest 'aha' moment this year." Samantha said that understanding the phenomenon of posttraumatic growth "helped me let go of my guilt for becoming the woman, mother, professional I want to become after the tragic loss of [Jake] . . . we talked about others who have grown from their loss, and the resources on the topic you provided allowed me to acknowledge that this is real and I am living it."

Samantha now recounts how, "[a]s simple as it seems, just meeting with you gave me strength and courage. I had to leave the boys, get on a train and spend the day in the city. I had to commit to something on my calendar. The first meeting we had I went right back on the train. As meetings progressed I found my favorite little Italian restaurant around the corner and enjoyed lunch by myself. I . . . now spend the day in the city by myself and love it. Having lunch by myself used to terrify me . . . now I smile to myself at how far I have come."

In the year since, she has gone on to reinvigorate her career as a marketing consultant and applied to graduate school to pursue a new professional direction in real estate. She speaks with pride of her newfound ability to forgive the fury she held towards those who disappointed her so deeply and criticized her so harshly; to cultivate new relationships with people she once feared would judge her because of her husband's suicide; to be the mother she knows her children need; and to make choices in the best interests of herself and her children on her own terms without being driven by fear and guilt.

Conclusions and Reflections

Initially, Samantha chose not to share the actual text of her *What a year it's been* journaling exercise, although we spoke at some length about her experience writing it and the insights she'd gleaned. When I sought her consent to submit this case study (ironically, almost exactly a year since our first contact), she offered to send it to me. Her cover email read, "Cried through this one . . . thank you for helping me get here. Reading this is not only amazing but scary because almost all of it is true."

Has she found meaning in her loss? Her words (personal communication, October 17, 2015), originally written a year ago yet perfectly describing the present, speak poignantly for themselves:

What a year it's been . . .
I have found happiness in daily life again.
I am balancing my life . . . and am happy and fulfilled.
I am proud of what I am doing with my career.
I accept that this is my life and I am living it to the fullest.
I finally feel like I have become the woman I always wanted to become.
I am proud of myself for finding me.

I cried through this one, too.

Joanne L. Harpel, MPhil, JD, *is the president of Coping After Suicide. A world-renowned expert on suicide bereavement and postvention, Ms. Harpel works with families and communities and trains clinicians, clergy, school personnel and other professionals. The survivor of her brother's suicide, she was recruited in 2001 by the world's largest suicide prevention organization to create the most well-respected array of resources in the field, including International Survivors of Suicide Loss Day, which takes place in 300 cities worldwide. Recipient of the American Association of Suicidology's Survivor of the Year Award, she has spoken on Capitol Hill, and for the American Psychiatric Association, the American Academy of Child & Adolescent Psychiatry, the New York State School Boards Association, and the Suicide Prevention Coalition of Colorado. Ms. Harpel has trained chaplains for the U.S. Department of Veterans Affairs and psychologists for the Korean Police Agency, and has collaborated with organizations from the National Institute of Mental Health to Columbia University's School of Social Work to HBO.*

REFERENCES

Baugher, B., & Jordan, J. (2002). *After suicide loss: Coping with your grief.* Des Moines, WA: Author.

Fine, C. (1997). *No time to say goodbye: Surviving the suicide of a loved one.* New York, NY: Doubleday.

Jordan, J. R., & McIntosh, J. (Eds.) (2011). *Grief after suicide: Understanding the consequences and caring for the survivors.* New York, NY: Routledge.

Mohr, T. (2104). *Playing big: Find your voice, your mission, your message.* New York, NY: Gotham Books.

Moore, M. *Post traumatic growth: Positive changes in the aftermath of crisis.* Retrieved from www.posttraumaticgrowth.com.

Neimeyer, R. (Ed.). (2012). *Techniques of grief therapy: Creative practices for counseling the bereaved.* New York, NY: Routledge.

Personal communications: November 19, 2014; November 20, 2014; May 21, 2015; October 26, 2015; and October 27, 2015.

Tedeschi, R., & Calhoun, C (2004). Posttraumatic growth: Conceptual foundations and empirical evidence. *Psychological Inquiry 15*, 1-18.

CHAPTER 14

The Impact of Military Culture on Suicide Prevention and Postvention: A Family Perspective

Kim Ruocco

S uicide is a complicated topic with multiple factors that impact prevention, intervention, and postvention. When considering a death by suicide of a service member, one must understand military culture and the role it played in the death. When a young man or woman joins the service, he or she is initiated through a boot camp that focuses on overcoming and pushing through physical and emotional pain. "Pain is weakness leaving the body" are words to live by. This saying implies that the more pain that can be tolerated, the stronger one is. It is a quality that a service member values throughout his or her career. Initial training also focuses on the importance of peers. Bonds are created and cemented through hardship, and a brotherhood develops where service members would literally give up their lives for their peers. With this bond grows a responsibility for the well-being of one's battle buddies and a fear of letting them down. Sayings such as, "You are only as strong as your weakest link," have developed out of this mindset. Values such as honor, commitment, and sacrifice are also highly regarded. These values and ways of thinking are often protective factors for those who are healthy and thriving but can become risk factors for those who are injured, ill, or struggling.

The military lifestyle includes life events that can be highly stressful, such as frequent moves, separations from support systems for extended periods, and exposure to loss and traumatic events at home, during training, and when deployed in combat zones. Military families often are asked to start over with new schools, new friends and new homes; children must start over with teams, coaches, teachers and school curriculum. Family members often adopt the mindset and culture of their loved one who is serving. Like service members, families are expected to be resilient and think of others first. Families learn quickly that a service member's reputation is important to his or her ability to be promoted, obtain security clearances, and be selected for prestigious positions. Spouses and children work hard to be loyal, supportive, and protective of their service member. This system can work well when the family is healthy and thriving, but when a service member is struggling, families are often torn between seeking help and risking possible negative consequences.

My personal story is a great example of how cultural expectations for a military family can increase risk and create conflict, which, if unresolved, can end in death by suicide.

When my husband joined the Marine Corps, he brought with him unresolved traumatic loss. He was determined to put that in his past and move forward with new purpose and identity. He learned quickly in The Basic School (basic training for Marines) that pushing through pain was highly valued. For example, he sprained his ankle early in the training but his ability to tape it up and excel in the physical testing was highly valued and admired by his fellow Marines. He eventually became a leader who seemed invincible.

My husband suffered his first bout of depression following a training accident in which several of his peers were killed. He saw this depression as a weakness or fault. He compared himself to others and wondered why he was not able to "suck it up" in the same way they were. As a spouse, I was very concerned. As a counselor, I knew he needed help. My husband was suffering, but more than emotional pain, he felt guilt and shame for the state he was in. We discussed getting help and he begged me not to tell anyone. He thought he should be able to push through this on his own. He thought it was his fault that he was suffering and that it was his responsibility to fix it. I was conflicted and had my own internal struggles. The last thing I wanted to do was make things worse for him or betray him. As a military spouse, I didn't know whom I could call or what would happen if I did. This fear kept me from doing anything. Eventually he was able to pull himself out of his depression. He told me, "I will never do that to you again." He said, "I can't believe I let that happen; I am such a weakling." This incident and how we viewed it would set the course for how we dealt with emotional and physical struggles going forward. My husband was struggling with the conflicting messages that had been drilled into his head at boot camp that he should be able to push through pain, and the leftover messages of his childhood that he was weak and his weakness could hurt someone. He was concerned that his illness was impeding his responsibility to take care of his family and peers. Like so many American military families, we thought we had to be strong, perfect, and resilient. We thought we needed to appear to be okay despite the consequences. The worst consequence is that we had accepted depression as a weakness and something to be hidden and toughed out, instead of an illness that needed treatment.

My husband enjoyed 10 years of success including three deployments, two promotions, and the birth of our two children before he suffered another depression.

He was an attack helicopter pilot and flew 75 successful combat missions in Iraq. He returned from Iraq safely, but three months later he died by suicide. When he returned from Iraq, he failed a routine flight test in the same helicopter he flew in combat. What is more dishonorable to a Marine than not being able to do his mission? Looking back, he may have been thinking of another military motto: "Death before dishonor." The last time I spoke with him, he admitted that he was struggling with depression and stress. I begged him to get help. After a long discussion, he agreed to go to behavioral health but he said to me, "I am going to lose everything." I tried to reassure him that it would be all right but he said, "People are going to think I am weak, they are going to think I am faking and just don't want to go back to Iraq." He continued by saying that he was going to "let everyone down." For years, my husband had avoided seeking treatment for fear that it would negatively impact his career. He could not understand why his peers had similar exposures but seemed okay. He worried that he was the weakest link and that if others knew, he would lose everything: his career, his sense of belonging, and his identity as a Marine. One of the last things he said to me was, "You all would be better off without me…." He promised that he was going to go to behavioral health but instead he took his own life.

In hindsight, I believe my husband was struggling with an internal conflict that he could not resolve. He knew he needed help but he didn't know how to get it without going against all the values he had come to live by.

Losing a loved one to suicide is confusing and the emotions can be overwhelming. For military families, some of those fears and emotions can be exacerbated by the culture. The military has a long tradition of honoring heroic deaths. This tradition puts a lot of emphasis on how one dies. For those service members who die in combat there are medals awarded, memorials erected, and streets and ballparks named after the deceased. In the case of suicide, the death may be seen as a selfish or even cowardly thing to do. Family members often fear that how their loved one died will be what is remembered instead of their extraordinary life of service and sacrifice.

Military families also experience additional losses following the death of a loved one. They must move out of military housing, often away from other military families who have become close. Children of the fallen often attend schools on base but must move to the civilian world where there is much less understanding of the military lifestyle, stressors, and losses. Loss of identity is another common issue. As a military spouse, I was often referred to as "Major Ruocco's wife." With this came an expected role and respect. After his death, I struggled to figure out who my support system should be and where I fit in.

Military families are resilient and proud but sometimes these characteristics can get in the way of healing when their service member dies by suicide. The shame and guilt can cause them to recluse themselves and resist care. My first inclination was to hunker down with my children and get through this like we had gotten through every other challenge. As I thought of my husband's life, his service, and his sacrifices, I found that I just couldn't let it end this way. I felt a strong desire to make meaning out of my husband's death. I found that the first step was to reach out to others who had similar losses. Peer-based support provided hope that I could survive this, and a new sense of belonging that I craved.

As I moved along in my grief journey, I found that using the lessons I learned to help others also helped me to heal. I believe that telling my husband's story can possibly keep another family from suffering such a horrific loss. My husband would have given his life for any of his Marines and I feel like I am continuing his mission. Possibly preventing another family's tragedy provided some meaning to his death and a new sense of purpose for me. For the past 10 years, I have been building programs for survivors of military suicide loss. I have witnessed these families come for support to the Tragedy Assistance

Program for Survivors (TAPS) seemingly broken and lost, but if we focus on the many strengths of these amazing families and provide the comprehensive care they need, I have found that it is possible for them to not only survive a suicide loss but thrive.

Kim Ruocco, MCSW, is the Chief External Relations Officer for Suicide Prevention and Postvention for the Tragedy Assistance Program for Survivors (TAPS). Ms. Ruocco has been the keynote speaker at many national events and is regularly quoted in national newspapers on the topics of suicide, military culture, mental illness, PTSD, and Department of Veterans Affairs and Department of Defense policy matters. She assisted in the development of the Department of Defense Suicide Prevention Office (DSPO) Postvention Toolkit and was a reviewer for the current national strategy for postvention. She and her sons were lead participants in the Sesame Street When Families Grieve *video which is distributed internationally to families who have a recent death. Ms. Ruocco created a team of peer-professionals who provide care and comfort to nearly 5000 survivors of military suicide. Ms. Ruocco is currently the co-lead on the National Action Alliance Military and Family Task Force and a member of the National Expert Advisory Panel for Research. She is also the surviving widow of Marine Corp Major John Ruocco, who died by suicide in 2005.*

CHAPTER 15

You were born, still
The Search for Meaning in Perinatal Loss

Robert A. Neimeyer

CASE DESCRIPTION

Three months after the stillbirth of her fourth biological child, Cara found herself encased in an anguishing and isolating grief. She spent hours each day weeping in her bedroom as she struggled to comply with internalized familial and cultural values and carry on as a pillar of strength for her African American family and community. Compounding her suffering over the simultaneous birth and death of her baby girl, the concurrent accidental pregnancy of Cara's 16-year-old daughter, Jasmine, aroused a tangle of powerful emotions, including anger at a daughter she did not know was sexually active, guilt about not protecting her from this unwanted pregnancy, jealousy about a teen mother bringing to term an unexpected child while she had lost a longed-for infant at seven months of gestation, and a sense of injustice in relation to God and the universe for permitting such a perversion of fate. Finally, finding herself unable to work, study, or function more than minimally, she pursued counseling with me to seek some meaning in a seemingly senseless loss.

STATEMENT OF PROBLEM

At one level, Cara's problems were obvious enough. She contended with images of mothers and healthy infants at seemingly every turn; her relationships with her pregnant daughter and best friend had almost utterly lapsed since the death of her child; and she experienced profound sleep disruption with repetitive dreams of searching for her baby. At another level, Cara's problem was both subtler and more pervasive, as she struggled with a new and darker view of life, one that shattered her "assumptive world" with its associated beliefs in life's predictability, the world's benevolence, and her own ability to control relevant outcomes (Janoff-Bulman & Berger, 2000), even that of her own pregnancy.

ANALYSIS

Viewed through a constructivist lens, grieving entails an effort to reaffirm or reconstruct a world of meaning that has been challenged by loss (Neimeyer, 2002). More specifically, bereavement can be seen as presenting two profound narrative challenges: (1) to process the *event story* of the death itself and its implications for our ongoing life, and (2) to access the *back story* of the relationship with the deceased in order to restore a measure of attachment security (Neimeyer & Thompson, 2014). Both forms of meaning making proved daunting for Cara, as the sudden and unexplained death *in utero* of her seemingly viable child traumatically violated the self-narrative she had been living out, while also depriving her of any history with a living child on which she could draw to reconstruct their attachment. As a result, she found herself alternating between flashbacks to the birth on the one hand and experiential avoidance of cues of the loss, including her daughter Jasmine, on the other, both of which are classic posttraumatic symptoms. Likewise, she was preoccupied with corrosive yearning for her infant and withdrawing in resentment and self-protection from other potentially supportive relationships, both core symptoms of complicated grief (Shear et al., 2011).

GOALS OF COUNSELING

An extensive and growing evidence base has demonstrated that a struggle for meaning plays a cardinal role in (a) predicting anticipatory grief before the death in the context of palliative care (Burke et al., 2015), (b) predicting both contemporaneous and subsequent complications in bereavement in diverse groups of mourners losing loved ones by a range of causes (Coleman & Neimeyer, 2010; Holland, Currier, & Neimeyer, 2014), and (c) mediating the impact of other risk factors such as violent death loss (Currier, Holland, & Neimeyer, 2006) and spiritual crisis (Lichtenthal, Burke, & Neimeyer, 2011) on complicated grief symptomatology. Moreover, an inability to make sense of the loss has been found to be a leading predictor of anguishing grief among bereaved parents (Keesee, Currier, & Neimeyer, 2008).

In keeping with this meaning reconstruction approach (Neimeyer, 2014), I listened to Cara's verbal, coverbal and nonverbal signals of both *need* and *readiness* to address the traumatic impact of her child's death, as well as to reorganize the bond with her deceased infant by constructing a viable back story of the child's brief life. I also sought to help her meet and overcome the impediments to a reaffirmation of other family relationships while drawing on the resources of her community and spiritual convictions. Thus, at levels ranging from the personal through the relational to the broadly social and cultural (Neimeyer, Klass, & Dennis, 2014), I joined her in revisiting the narrative of the loss and the socially constructed framework of meanings that it had shaken, with the goal of reconstructing a viable life narrative that offered meaning and orientation, even in the wake of tragic loss.

INTERVENTION STRATEGY

As an attachment-informed grief therapy, a meaning reconstruction approach strives to assist the client with (a) *emotion regulation* through offering attuned presence, breath work and guided imagery, (b) *mindfulness* through acknowledging feelings without judgment or attachment, and (c) *mentalizing* through reflecting upon her own psychological state and that of relevant others to foster compassionate understanding (Kosminsky & Jordan, 2016). Supplementing this consistent attention to *presence* and *process*, I also consciously introduced specific *procedures* to facilitate Cara's efforts to process the event story of her loss and to access a more viable continuing bond to her child, without grief being the only tether (Neimeyer, 2012a).

In the third of our six sessions, Cara brought in an envelope of printed photos taken by her sister during her hospitalization for her daughter's delivery, photos that she herself had never been ready to see but felt she was ready to see now. I asked if she would prefer that I look at them first, briefly describing each one, then asked if she felt prepared to view that particular image. Without hesitation she gratefully thrust the envelope at me, saying, "You can look at them first." My role as an emotional modulator of exposure to a difficult loss narrative was consistent with the practice of presence described above, as well as with evidence-informed "restorative retelling" procedures for helping clients integrate the story of tragic death (Neimeyer, 2012b; Rynearson & Salloum, 2011).

I think of retelling procedures as involving three interbraided processes: bracing, pacing and facing. *Bracing* entails first grounding the client in the session through establishing a strong empathic bond, as well as by revisiting and reaffirming the personal, familial, and philosophic or spiritual resources on which he or she can draw in tolerating a reencounter with the narrative of the loss. *Pacing* involves dosing exposure to the story, both by slowing down into its difficult details, and by staying present to them, without avoidance, to notice and process what arises. Finally, *facing* implies compassionate mutual confrontation with the experience and its associated meanings and emotions, with the therapist serving as witness, as the client seeks some level of empowerment in a tragically disempowering event. In practical terms, this often requires devoting 30 or more minutes of the therapeutic hour to a close review of the story of the death, visualizing the scenes as they unfold, with or without photographic cues. The therapist gently diverts the client's attention to the *external, internal*, and *reflexive* narrative, that is, to what happened, how it felt, and what it meant, through timely recursive questions. Subsequent in-session and between-session processing under carefully negotiated conditions of safety (e.g., further therapeutic journaling in a comforting space about feelings or insights prompted by the review) then further facilitate the integration of the experience (Neimeyer, 2012b).

In response to Cara's heartfelt statement about the photos ("I saved them to open them with you"), I shared briefly my genuine sense of being moved by her trust. I then took a breath, slowly released it, and withdrew the stack of pictures, the first of which depicted a tiny infant in what I described as a "white bed with flowers." "Her casket," Cara corrected, leaning forward slightly to take the photo. She drew the photo close as she began to speak of the funeral for her child, who she had named "Spirit," because she came to her as a spiritual being rather than a living baby. As I briefly described each image and passed them to Cara, we discovered that we were telling the story of Spirit's birth and burial in reverse chronological order, as that was the way the photos had been stacked in the envelope. This sequencing proved oddly appropriate, allowing us to begin with the viewing of the infant in the casket, and then to back up, step by step, into Cara's intimate embrace with her daughter's lifeless body immediately following her birth, as her husband's strong hand rested on the baby's tiny form. "Poor thing," she intoned, "she never had a chance."

Throughout the 30 minutes of emotional narration we tacked repeatedly from the *what* of the account to its *how* and *why*, its associated emotions and meanings. Cara acknowledged her self-protective tendency to "step out" to a tolerable distance of emotional neutrality, as she also gradually accepted the opportunity to bravely "step in" to more contact with her grief. In the course of the retelling, two significant embellishments occurred. In the midst of reviewing the funeral, Cara brought out a carefully folded program with Spirit's name and date of birth and handed it to me to read a moving dedication coauthored by her and her sister, entitled *Born, Still.* "They will say that you did not live and will register you as a stillborn child. But for me, you lived all that time in my womb.... Now I know that you are in the grace of God, in his sight, his perfect little angel. I know that for us, *you were born, still.* We will carry you with us forever, my child, my love. You will always be a part of all of us. You were always ours and are ours now. Death and life are the same. You were born, still." As I read the words aloud with her encouragement, Cara conferred deep meaning on the loss and on her child, despite the tragic prematurity of her birth and death.

Returning to the retelling, Cara caressed the professional hospital photograph of her child's bruised face ("almost deformed," she noted, by laying lifeless on one side in her womb), as we also affirmed Spirit's delicate beauty. After completing the moving review of the photos, Cara reached for a final envelope. "Now I have one more image to show you," she said, removing the ultrasound taken in her fourth month of pregnancy, when her baby seemed fully viable. Pointing to an image partially eclipsing the profile of the fetus, she traced the clearly discernible form of a woman in a robe, in movement as if she were walking, with impassive mouth and vacant eyes staring straight out at the viewer. Cara recalled how she had asked the doctor whether the uncanny form might have been the umbilical cord, a possibility he dismissed. Later, discussing the meaning of the spectral woman with her family, she was met with reassurance from her mother, a scream from her sister, and joking dismissals from others. But for Cara, the image was no laughing matter when, three months later, her baby died.

The death, in combination with what she took to be a sinister image, initiated for Cara the sort of crisis of faith we have often documented in association with complicated grief (Burke & Neimeyer, 2014; Burke, Neimeyer, McDevitt-Murphy, Ippolito, & Roberts, 2011). Although the restorative retelling of the death narrative had begun to assuage some of the anxiety of the event story, this deeper challenge to her core spiritual meanings remained. Nearing the session's end, I noted the many questions and angry feelings that Cara seemed to direct to the ghostly apparition, and asked if she might consider writing a letter to the figure, expressing these directly, and then simply sensing what responses might come. Cara agreed, and returned in the fourth session with a riveting letter, which she handed to me to read aloud. "What are you?" she began. "Where did you come from? Why would God bless me with life, only to take it from me?" In sentence after sentence, Cara poured out her grief, her anger, her sense of divine injustice.

The session set the stage for subsequent family meaning making (Nadeau, 1997) with a wise old aunt who had studied theology and who suggested that, "when you die, one of your ancestors will come to get you." "But I don't recognize this person," Cara protested. "But you weren't here a hundred years ago, so you don't know who that is," the aunt replied. Something in these words struck a chord for Cara, who began to undergo a dramatic revision of her spiritual cosmology. Not only, in her view, was the spectral woman in the ultrasound "not an evil being," but the axis of the universe had shifted, in a sense, from a cosmology in which she had placed herself at the center of the universe, to one in which she was much smaller, and the universe much bigger, and one filled with other people whose suffering was equivalent to her own. This revised spiritual frame was further reinforced by reflective writing she did between sessions, as she consolidated her continuing bond to Spirit by tracing the profound "life imprint" of her short existence (Neimeyer, 2010) on her own coping abilities and values, leading her to reach out to several family members and, uncharacteristically, directly affirm her love for them. This was most strikingly evident in relation to her teenage daughter, Jasmine, who she had nearly totally avoided as the girl gave birth to her own baby and who clearly needed her mother's care and guidance in an uncertain new phase of her life.

Embracing her daughter once again after an anguishing three months of distancing, Cara affirmed her belief in Jasmine's ability, with support, to build a life of purpose and become "a great young woman." Most touching of all was Cara's closing anticipation, offered with a broad and genuine smile, of lulling her new granddaughter to sleep in the rocking chair she had purchased for Spirit. Finally, Cara summarized her substantial reduction in complicated grief symptoms and a stunning array of indicators of posttraumatic growth (Calhoun & Tedeschi, 2006) arising from Spirit's death and her integration of it into a new life narrative, including a decision to return to school and change her major to counseling. As we concluded our final session, I shared my pride in her growth through grief, and my awe in her reconstruction of a life of meaning in the face of challenging loss.

CONCLUSIONS AND REFLECTIONS

As a relatively new orientation to grief therapy, meaning reconstruction is not so much a distinctive theory competing with others, as it is a meta-theory that cuts across many contemporary theories of bereavement. As such, it has inspired and integrated a great variety of creative clinical procedures for assessing and intervening in meaning in the wake of tragic loss, a few of which are illustrated in my therapy with Cara. Readers interested in viewing the entirety to our therapy can find videos of all sessions published by the American Psychological Association (Neimeyer, 2008), just as those interested in exploring scores of specific meaning-oriented techniques of grief therapy may consult recent manuals compiled for this purpose (Neimeyer, 2012c, 2016; Thompson & Neimeyer, 2014).

Robert A. Neimeyer, PhD, is a professor of psychology, University of Memphis, where he also maintains an active clinical practice. Neimeyer has published 30 books, including Techniques of Grief Therapy: Assessment and Intervention *and* Grief and the Expressive Arts: Practices for Creating Meaning, *the latter with Barbara Thompson, and serves as editor of the journal* Death Studies. *The author of nearly 500 articles and book chapters and a frequent workshop presenter, he is currently working to advance a more adequate theory of grieving as a meaning-making process. Neimeyer served as president of the Association for Death Education and Counseling (ADEC) and chair of the International Work Group for Death, Dying, and Bereavement. In recognition of his scholarly contributions, he has been made a Fellow of Clinical Psychology by the American Psychological Association and given Lifetime Achievement Awards by both ADEC and the International Network on Personal Meaning. More information and resources can be found at www.robertneimeyerphd.com.*

REFERENCES

Burke, L. A., & Neimeyer, R. A. (2014). Complicated spiritual grief I: Relation to complicated grief symptomatology following violent death bereavement. *Death Studies, 38,* 259-267. doi: 10.1080/07481187.2013.829372

Burke, L. A., Neimeyer, R. A., Smigelsky, M. A., Gibson, B. W., Ali, K. S., & Clark, K. A. (2015). Risk factors for anticipatory grief in family members of terminally ill veterans receiving palliative care services. *Journal of Social Work in End-of-Life and Palliative Care, 11:*3-4, 244-266. doi: 10.1080/15524256.2015.1110071.

Burke, L. A., Neimeyer, R. A., McDevitt-Murphy, M. E., Ippolito, M. R., & Roberts, J. M. (2011). Faith in the wake of homicide: Spiritual crisis and bereavement distress in an African American sample. *International Journal for the Psychology of Religion, 21,* 289-307.

Calhoun, L., & Tedeschi, R. G. (Eds.). (2006). *Handbook of posttraumatic growth.* Mahwah, NJ: Lawrence Erlbaum Associates.

Coleman, R. A., & Neimeyer, R. A. (2010). Measuring meaning: Searching for and making sense of spousal loss in later life. *Death Studies, 34,* 804-834.

Currier, J. M., Holland, J. M., & Neimeyer, R. A. (2006). Sense making, grief and the experience of violent loss: Toward a mediational model. *Death Studies, 30,* 403-428.

Holland, J. M., Currier, J. M. , & Neimeyer, R. A. (2014). Validation of the Integration of Stressful Life Experiences Scale – Short Form in a bereaved sample. *Death Studies, 38,* 234-238. doi: 10.1080/07481187.2013.829369

Janoff-Bulman, R., & Berger, A. R. (2000). The other side of trauma. In J. H. Harvey & E. D. Miller (Eds.), *Loss and trauma.* Philadelphia, PA: Brunner Mazel.

Keesee, N. J., Currier, J. M., & Neimeyer, R. A. (2008). Predictors of grief following the death of one's child: The contribution of finding meaning. *Journal of Clinical Psychology, 64,* 1145-1163.

Kosminsky, P., & Jordan, J. R. (2016). *Attachment informed grief therapy.* New York, NY: Routledge.

Lichtenthal, W. G., Burke, L. A., & Neimeyer, R. A. (2011). Religious coping and meaning-making following the loss of a loved one. *Counseling and Spirituality, 30,* 113-136.

Nadeau, J. W. (1997). *Families making sense of death.* Newbury Park, CA: Sage.

Neimeyer, R. A. (2002). *Lessons of loss: A guide to coping.* Memphis, TN: Center for the Study of Loss and Transition.

Neimeyer, R. A. (2008). Constructivist psychotherapy over time [DVD]. Washington, DC: American Psychological Association.

Neimeyer, R. A. (2010). The life imprint. In H. Rosenthal (Ed.), *Favorite counseling and therapy techniques.* New York, NY: Routledge.

Neimeyer, R. A. (2012a). Presence, process and procedure: A relational frame for technical proficiency in grief therapy. In R. A. Neimeyer (Ed.), *Techniques of grief therapy* (pp. 3-11). New York, NY: Routledge.

Neimeyer, R. A. (2012b). Retelling the narrative of the death. In R. A. Neimeyer (Ed.), *Techniques of grief therapy* (pp. 86-90). New York, NY: Routledge.

Neimeyer, R. A. (2014). Meaning in bereavement. In R. E. Anderson (Ed.), *World suffering and quality of life.* New York, NY: Springer.

Neimeyer, R. A. (Ed.). (2012c). *Techniques of grief therapy: Creative practices for counseling the bereaved.* New York, NY: Routledge.

Neimeyer, R. A. (Ed.). (2016). *Techniques of grief therapy: Assessment and intervention.* New York, NY: Routledge.

Neimeyer, R. A., Klass, D., & Dennis, M. R. (2014). A social constructionist account of grief: Loss and the narration of meaning. *Death Studies, (38),* 485-498.

Neimeyer, R. A., & Thompson, B. E. (2014). Meaning making and the art of grief therapy. In B. E. Thompson & R. A. Neimeyer (Eds.), *Grief and the expressive arts: Practices for creating meaning* (pp. 3-13). New York, NY: Routledge.

Rynearson, E. K., & Salloum, A. (2011). Restorative retelling: Revisiting the narrative of violent death. In R. A. Neimeyer, D. Harris, H. Winokuer, & G. Thornton (Eds.), *Grief and bereavement in contemporary society: Bridging research and practice* (pp. 177-188). New York, NY: Routledge.

Shear, M. K., Simon, N., Wall, M., Zisook, S., Neimeyer, R. A., Duan, N.,...Keshaviah, A. (2011). Complicated grief and related bereavement issues for DSM-5. *Depression and Anxiety, 28*, 103-117.

Thompson, B. E., & Neimeyer, R. A. (Eds.). (2014). *Grief and the expressive arts: Practices for creating meaning.* New York, NY: Routledge.

CHAPTER 16

Meaning Making Following the Death of an Adult Child

Zaneta M. Gileno

CASE DESCRIPTION

At the age of 52, Katelyn was a single mother of three sons. She maintained a full-time career as well as a part-time job to make ends meet. As a true member of the "sandwich generation," she was taking care of her mother who had a terminal illness while caring for a younger son still living at home.

Katelyn was shy and reserved but hard-working. In her job at a medical office, she did not have the courage to greet patients; instead, she would hand them a pen and point to the clipboard indicating they should sign in. Despite her timid nature, she led her family, served in her church community, and supported a friend who struggled with addiction by establishing a support group.

Katelyn's son Cale enlisted in the military following the events of 9/11. She felt proud of her son but alone in her role as a military mother. She lacked someone with whom she could discuss her concerns and fully understand the burden she carried. Cale served one tour of duty in Afghanistan and was killed in action during a second tour in Iraq. When she learned Cale was killed, she said her world shattered.

Military culture includes a strong commitment to the mission, which can build solidarity within the group. The loss of a military member may shatter this effect (Harrington-LaMorie & McDevitt-Murphy, 2011). Bonnie Carroll, President and Founder of the Tragedy Assistance Program for Survivors (TAPS) states, "The day your service member joined the military is the day you, too, joined the military – particularly if you are a close family member." Cale had always expressed to Katelyn that they both were part of something greater than themselves.

They spoke weekly during each of his deployments; Cale told Katelyn that he joined the military so he could send someone else home. Just prior to his death, Cale posted on social media that he had done just that, and Katelyn immediately took comfort in his statement. The night she learned of Cale's death, she was surprised to feel pride along with her sadness. After his death, Katelyn leaned on understanding that Cale died for a cause and also relied on her spirituality and belief in God. The purpose of this case study is to illustrate the role of meaning making in Katelyn's life and its likely contribution to her posttraumatic growth.

Statement of Problem

In the face of her traumatic loss, Katelyn found herself unable to accomplish all of the tasks she felt she needed to complete. The sudden loss of her son affected Katelyn's ability to work and find joy in life. She gave up both her part-time job and facilitating the addiction support group due to her self-described emotional instability. She put all of her energy into caring for her ailing mother and adolescent son. Although she continued caring for them and ensuring that their needs were met, her prior feelings of being the only mother with a son at war were now compounded by feeling like the only parent who had ever lost a child.

Analysis

Katelyn's social circle diminished as she pulled away from her work obligations and personal relationships. Katelyn originally lacked peer support as a military mother; as a grieving mother, this isolation was even more palpable. The impact of a child's death, which is understood to be a tremendously devastating loss, can be compounded over time, leading to complicated grief, where the griever "is overwhelmed, resorts to maladaptive behavior, or remains interminably in the state of grief without progression of the mourning process towards completion" (Worden, 2009). However, thanatology experts believe that 80% of bereaved parents experience normative grief. Normative grief can be described as a lack of energy and social withdrawal; feelings of confusion, sadness, and disbelief may also be prevalent (Bonanno & Lilienfeld, 2008).

Living in a rural area, she found services difficult to access. The Casualty Assistance Officer assigned to support Katelyn following her son's death immediately connected her to counseling resources but the providers were located more than an hour from her home. Family obligations made it impractical to utilize the resources, so she placed her desire for therapeutic support on the back burner.

GOALS OF COUNSELING

"There are varying types of support after a loss, both practical and emotional, and all of them can help you on your journey" (Harrington-LaMorie, 2015). A therapeutic approach that would allow Katelyn to open to the reality of the death of her son and also address her needs as a caregiver to her ailing mother was necessary, as was a connection to peer-based support. At first, being a caregiver inhibited both her need for and her ability to access support. According to Rando, "If the mourner perceives that support is unavailable, that it is available and not forthcoming, or that his loss is not socially acknowledged, the perception can have a profound impact on coping and may constitute a high-risk factor for complicated mourning" (Rando, 1993, p. 496). But when she did reach out for support, Katelyn found such support was available. According to Rando, "If the mourner perceives the world as providing support for mourning, that perception is an extremely positive factor" (Rando, 1993, p. 495). For Katelyn, both her role as a caregiver, as well as the support she received, seemed to be positive factors. Katelyn also followed a religious practice, which she was encouraged to embrace following the death of her son. Encouragement to seek the strongholds of friendship was also instrumental.

INTERVENTION STRATEGY

A few months following Cale's death, Katelyn felt it was time to seek help, and through an online search located the Tragedy Assistance Program for Survivors (TAPS). The mission of TAPS is to provide immediate and long-term support to those grieving the death of a loved one in the Armed Forces. Through this comprehensive service organization, Katelyn was connected to individual counseling, support groups, and peer-based emotional assistance. In addition, Katelyn was afforded the opportunity to participate in an experiential retreat with other bereaved military parents.

TAPS connected Katelyn to a local hospice worker in the community who offered one-to-one therapeutic support. Upon their initial meeting, Katelyn opened up about her son's motivation for serving in the military. The therapist disclosed she would not be able to focus on grief work with Katelyn because she herself had a nephew who had just returned safely from Iraq and she worried about the emotional entanglement this would cause. Yet, the coincidence of Cale serving to bring another service member home, and the therapist's family member making it home alive, bonded the two. Despite the professional disclosure that she would not be able to fully engage in grief work, Katelyn and the therapist formed a strong helping alliance, which continues to this day. This therapist embraced what Wolfelt refers to as, "Supplemental of the soul...life-giving, hope filled... incorporating not only the mind and body, but more importantly the soul and the spirit" (Wolfelt, 2014).

Professionals working in the field of trauma, "...have realized that the resulting effects of trauma range from acute stress disorder (ASD), posttraumatic stress disorder (PTSD), and other serious psychopathological responses, to existential crisis, to posttraumatic growth" (Levers, 2012). During treatment, Katelyn was diagnosed with Minor Depressive Disorder; this depression had lasted for more than two weeks and was episodic in nature. According to *The Diagnostic and Statistical Manual of Mental Disorders* (4th ed.), "Mild episodes are characterized by the presence of only five or six depressive symptoms and either mild disability or the capacity to function normally but with substantial and unusual effort" (American Psychiatric Association, 2000). Katelyn took an antidepressant for about five years and found it to be quite helpful.

During therapy, Katelyn focused on her emotional distress surrounding her mother's terminal illness and her caregiving responsibilities in the wake of a traumatic loss. A breakthrough took place for Katelyn when the therapist suggested that the experience was somewhat similar to her own as a teenager, bringing up questions about what life would be like from here on. Katelyn recognized that she had never fully taken the opportunity to decide her own life path because she always did what was expected of her. As the therapist described the process of adjusting to a new normal, Katelyn made a conscious decision to look within herself. She stated, "I looked at her and said, 'If I have the choice, I am going to change who I am. If I have to rewrite who I am, I am going to make myself better.' This was life altering for me." Deciding to change some fundamental beliefs and goals became a key impetus (Tedeschi & Calhoun, 2004).

Connecting with other parents who had lost a child also was helpful for Katelyn. She engaged in a manualized, 10-week support group. Manualized treatments offer a structured, therapeutic approach. These evidence-based treatments follow an outline and lend themselves well to a self-help model. Manualized treatments can be very effective and give new practitioners guidelines within which to work (Embry, 2008). The support group provided Katelyn the opportunity to learn about her unique journey. The manual taught her she could not, as Wolfelt states, "… go around the pain that is the wilderness of our grief. Instead, we must journey all through it, sometimes shuffling along the less strenuous side paths, sometimes plowing directly into the dark center" (Wolfelt, 2003). Through connecting with other parents, Katelyn felt less isolated in her grief. She created a strong bond with another mother who also had lost a son. Katelyn recalled feeling guilt that Cale was viewed as a hero in the community because he had died serving his country; other parents in the group were not afforded the same experience. But while she felt very welcomed in the group, she also felt that her grief journey was somehow different.

TAPS invited Katelyn to a retreat specifically for parents who had lost a child in the military. She recalled pleading with her employer for additional time off, knowing it would change her life, although she was not sure how. She was able to connect in a truly understanding environment where "survivors learn that they share emotions and experiences, and normalizing these feelings with others can be a powerful impetus for hope and change" (Gileno, 2014). The TAPS Parent's Retreat also gave Katelyn the chance to experience nature and adventure while grieving. This unique opportunity to connect with other surviving military parents in a safe and supportive setting forever altered Katelyn's grief journey. She reported, "We cried. We laughed. We shared about our living children. We shared stories of our fallen children. We shared about our dreams for the future… I had found my family. This event changed my world as drastically as my son's death, only in a positive manner."

Conclusions and Reflections

Katelyn immediately sought meaning in her son's death from the moment she opened the front door and learned he had died. She leaned heavily on her son's desire to serve in the aftermath of 9/11 and the message from his social media post regarding accomplishing his goal to send another soldier home. She took pride in the fact she was the mother of a war hero. This foundation allowed her to reconcile her grief in a tangible, life-affirming way. We come to reconcile in our grief journeys when the full reality of the death becomes a part of us (Wolfelt, 2015). Katelyn stated, "I was traumatized and I will never be the same. The fact is, my son lived and my son died. I didn't have to die with him and I chose not to." Her motivation to live through his spirit allowed her to reach out and gain social supports from her new peers. Doka reports that the spiritual connections our clients experience following the death of a loved one contribute to continuing bonds (Doka, 2015). Social supports appear to boost posttraumatic growth, "because they provide discussion of perspective, offering of beliefs, and the use of metaphor to explain experience" (Tedeschi & Calhoun, 2004).

Research shows that many trauma survivors do not return to baseline following their traumatic event, nor do they just accept what has happened. As researcher Stephen Joseph states, "They feel it made them better human beings than they would have been without it. And it made them wiser and willing to take the risk of being more fully alive" (as cited in Graves, 2015). Now Katelyn is more active in her community, more readily engages in conversation with strangers, and organizes events to honor the fallen. Cale's death brought her to the depths, and in the midst of her turmoil, she reconstructed life and meaning she would not have dreamed possible prior to her trauma.

Zaneta M. Gileno began her social work career as a professional in the child welfare system. Her efforts to reunite families and empower parents helped shape her as a practitioner. A graduate of Columbia University School of Social Work, Zaneta now serves as Director, Community-based Care for the Tragedy Assistance Program for Survivors (TAPS). As a grief professional, she offers direct survivor support, ensures the TAPS community of survivors is connected to grief counseling and support groups, and establishes and maintains the network of TAPS own support group model. In addition, she oversees internal professional education as well as TAPS professional development offerings.

REFERENCES

American Psychiatric Association. (2000). *Diagnostic and statistical manual of mental disorders* (4th ed.). Washington, DC: Author.

Bonanno G. A., & Lilienfield, S. O. (2008). When grief counseling is effective and when it's not. *Professional Psychology: Research and Practice, 39*(3), 377-378.

Carroll, B. & Wolfelt, A. (2015). *Healing your grieving heart after a military death: 100 practical ideas for friends and family.* Fort Collins, CO: Companion Press.

Doka, K. (August 11, 2015). Paranormal experiences at the end of life and after death [Webinar]. Washington, DC: Hospice Foundation of America.

Embry, R. (2008). Lecture, Columbia University School of Social Work, New York, NY.

Gileno, Z. (2014). TAPS care groups: Finding safety in numbers. *TAPS Magazine, 20*(2), 24-25.

Graves, G. (2015, July). Why some people really do grow stronger in the face of tragedy. *The Oprah Magazine.* Retrieved from http://www.huffingtonpost.com/2015/07/15/posttraumatic-growth_n_7796816.html?utm_hp_ref=own-happier

Harrington-LaMorie, J. , & McDevitt-Murphy, M. (2011). Traumatic death in the United States military: Initiating the dialogue on war-related loss. In R. A. Neimeyer, D. L. Harris, H. R. Winokuer, & G. F. Thornton (Eds.), *Grief and bereavement in contemporary society: Bridging research and practice* (pp. 261-272). New York, NY: Routledge/Taylor & Francis Group.

Harrington-LaMorie, J., Cohen, J., & Cozza, S. (2014). Caring for bereaved military family members. In S. Cozza, M. Goldenberg, & R. Ursano, R. (Eds.), *Care of military service members, veterans, and their families.* Washington, DC: American Psychiatric Publishing.

Harrington-LaMorie, J. (2015, Summer). Lean on me: Building your support network. *TAPS Magazine, 21*(2), 28-29.

Levers, L. (2012). An introduction to counseling survivors of trauma: Beginning to understand the context of trauma. In L. Levers (Ed.), *Trauma counseling and interventions* (pp. 1-22). New York, NY: Springer Publishing Company, LLC.

McCoyd, J., Walter, C. & Levers, L. (2012). Issues of loss and grief. In L. Levers (Ed.), *Trauma counseling and interventions* (pp. 77-97). New York, NY: Springer Publishing Company, LLC.

Neimeyer, R. A. & Sands, D. C. (2011). Meaning reconstruction in bereavement: From principles to practice. In R. A. Neimeyer, D. L. Harris, H. R. Winokuer, & G. F. Thornton (Eds.), *Grief and bereavement in contemporary society: Bridging research and practice* (pp. 9-22). New York, NY: Routledge/Taylor & Francis Group.

Pearlman, L., Wortman, C., Feuer, C., Farber, C., & Rando, T. (2014). *Treating traumatic bereavement: A practitioner's guide.* New York, NY: The Guilford Press.

Rando, T. (1993). *Treatment of complicated mourning.* Champaign, IL: Research Press.

Tedeschi, R. & Calhoun, L. (2004). Posttraumatic growth: Conceptual foundations and empirical evidence. *Psychological Inquiry, 5,* 1-18.

Wolfelt, A. (2003). *Understanding your grief: Ten essential touchstones for finding hope and healing your heart.* Fort Collins, CO: Companion Press.

Wolfelt, A. (2014). *Reframing PTSD as traumatic grief: How caregivers can companion traumatized grievers through catch-up mourning.* Fort Collins, CO: Companion Press.

Wolfelt, A. (2015). *The paradoxes of mourning: Healing your grief with three forgotten truths.* Fort Collins, CO: Companion Press.

Worden, J. (2009). *Grief counseling and grief therapy: A handbook for the mental health practioner (4th ed.).* New York, NY: Springer Publishing Company, LLC.

CHAPTER 17

The Use of Therapeutic Ritual

Kenneth J. Doka

CASE DESCRIPTION

Rosa was a 9-year-old girl who was being interviewed as part of a pre-adoptive evaluation. Her mother, Maria, was an IV-drug user who had died of AIDS. In the past four years, Rosa had gone in and out of foster care as her mom struggled first with addiction and then with both addiction and illness. Maria would emerge from rehab clean and sober, regain custody of her daughter, try hard to be a good mother, gradually fall into substance abuse, lose custody, return to the street, and eventually reenter rehab. Rosa was conceived out of wedlock and Maria had never identified Rosa's biological father.

A great source of stability in Rosa's life was her godmother, Carla, and her husband, Manny. They had been her foster parents and now planned to legally adopt her. Even when Rosa had returned to live with Maria, Carla and Manny always played a significant role in Rosa's life, supporting her emotionally and even financially. During the evaluation interview, the counselor asked Rosa where her mother was. Rosa replied that her mother was now a ghost. The counselor asked how one became a ghost. Rosa explained that if a person was very bad, that person went to hell, burned up, and became a skeleton. If the person was very good, she went to heaven and received angel wings. If the person was in between, she became a ghost. Further queried, Rosa indicated that ghosts had a second chance to be good or bad. Good ghosts would go to heaven, while bad ghosts would be sent to hell. The counselor recognized in Rosa's discussion her ambivalence toward her mother.

ANALYSIS

A significant issue for bereaved individuals is dealing with the complicated emotions generated by the loss (Worden, 2009). While some degree of ambivalence exists in most close relationships, intensely ambivalent relationships are often a complicating factor in grief (Rando, 1993; Worden, 2009).

Rosa's attachment to her mother was ambivalent. From early childhood, depending on where Maria was in her substance abuse cycle, she could be available or unavailable to Rosa. Maria would always emerge from rehab proudly claiming that her love for Rosa was the reason for her successful release, and affirming that she loved Rosa more than drugs. Yet, as Maria relapsed into substance abuse, Rosa could only conclude that drugs were her mother's first love. Moreover, while Maria was never violent toward Rosa, she would become neglectful once she relapsed.

Rosa's relationship with her foster family was far less complicated. Carla and Manny were attentive, concerned parents who always provided food, shelter, and emotional support. Their son, Ben, was a decade older than Carla. An only child, he doted on his "little sister." Rosa's only ambivalence to her foster and later, adoptive, family was the fact that she lacked some of the freedom she had at home. The family had strict rules governing school, bedtime, and other matters, and it was a much more structured environment than Rosa had at her mother's home. Yet, when Rosa did live with Maria, she missed the structure and found that she sometimes tried to impose it on herself.

Rosa's happiness with her foster family also contributed to her ambivalence. She wished for her mother's recovery but always dreaded being returned to her care. The fact that she wanted to stay at Carla and Manny's house made her feel guilty and disloyal. These feelings were exacerbated when Rosa learned that Maria had a life-threatening illness. As much as Rosa wished and prayed for her mother's health, she felt deeply comforted that she would now live permanently with Carla and Manny. This feeling not only aroused guilt but also anger, as Rosa struggled with the fact that her mother's drug use was the factor that caused her mother to "abandon her" (in her mind) to her foster family. To Rosa, if she preferred them to her own mother, Maria had only her substance abuse to blame.

Rosa found it difficult to address her ambivalent feelings even within her foster home. Carla had been close to Maria prior to her substance abuse difficulties. Carla also felt ambivalent. She deeply loved Rosa and Maria, and while she wanted to adopt Rosa, she also hoped Maria would transcend her problems. Carla discouraged any negative words about Maria, even from Rosa. When Maria was alive, Carla would describe her as ill and troubled and urged Rosa to pray for her mother's full recovery. After Maria's death, Carla would entreat Rosa to focus on the good memories.

GOALS OF COUNSELING

In counseling Rosa, it became clear that her ambivalence to her mother would be a major factor complicating her grief. The goal of counseling is to assist Rosa in resolving this ambivalence to help her move forward in her grief journey.

INTERVENTION STRATEGY

Rosa's counselor began by exploring her relationship with her mother. Sometimes the counselor used expressive therapeutic approaches, particularly art and play therapy. However, Rosa was a bright, verbal child, with a long experience in foster care of speaking with social workers and counselors, so she was far more open to talk therapy than many young children might be.

The counselor began to focus specifically on her ambivalence, asking Rosa questions such as: *What did you like about your mother? What did you dislike about her? What do you miss about your mom? What do you not miss? What did you like about living with your mom? What did you dislike?* Such questions are often effective with ambivalent relationships as they allow the client to first affirm positive feelings and memories as well as engaging more negative responses. In addition, the counselor worked with Carla and Manny to allow, model, and encourage Rosa to express her ambivalent feelings.

With these questions, Rosa was able to normalize her own sense of ambivalence, aided by Carla's sharing of her own ambivalent feelings. Rosa also recognized her mother's ambivalence about Rosa's relationship with Carla, Manny, and Ben. Rosa realized how hard it must have been for Maria to see other people raise her child, even as she was comforted by the fact that she was being raised by loving and caring friends. Rosa could even express gratitude for what she recognized as a sacrifice by her mother.

As Rosa worked with her ambivalent feelings the counselor understood that Rosa believed that it was time to find a way to allow her to forgive her mother. The counselor invited Rosa to plan a ritual to mark Maria's entry into heaven.

Rosa decided to cut out a full-length photograph of her mother and attach angel wings made of a doily. Since Maria had had such a chaotic lifestyle, there were few photographs available, but eventually Carla found a photo that could be used. When asked what was to be done with the photograph once the wings were attached, Rosa decided it should be burned so it would drift into heaven and Maria would receive it as a "welcome to heaven" gift.

CONCLUSIONS AND REFLECTIONS

As Rosa's story demonstrates, rituals can be an extremely powerful therapeutic tool in grief counseling. For example, research has indicated that funeral rituals can be highly therapeutic (Bolton & Camp, 1987, 1989; Doka, 1984; Gross & Klass, 1997; Rando, 1984; Reeves & Boersma, 1990). Funerals can offer meaningful activity at a chaotic time; provide opportunities to express and share memories and feelings; allow social support to be offered and received; and interpret spiritual beliefs about the loss. This value can be enhanced when funerals are participatory and personalized.

Gennep (1960) described the power of rituals in that they are liminal; they are transitional events that occur on the threshold between consciousness and unconsciousness. It is not unusual that during the course of a ritual, unconscious reactions can occur. Think, for example, of participating in a ritual and suddenly, without conscious reflection, experiencing goosebumps or tears. This liminality is evident in the ritual that Rosa designed. Even though Rosa has forgiven her mother and perceived her in heaven, her mother still had to "burn" in a purging fire that allowed her entry to heaven.

In discussing therapeutic ritual, Doka (2008) described four different types of rituals that can be used in grief counseling. Rosa participated in a *ritual of reconciliation*, a ritual designed to accept or offer forgiveness. *Rituals of affirmation* are designed to celebrate a legacy, to thank someone for the role that he or she had played in one's life. For example, a group home for adults with developmental disabilities designed a ritual called the Golden Circle. In this ritual, after a resident had died, the remaining residents would form a circle. Each person—both staff and residents—would simply acknowledge an attribute that they admired about the deceased individual.

Other rituals can be *rituals of transition*. A ritual of transition marks movement on an individual's journey with grief. Jason, a teenage boy, struggled with the fact that his father abandoned the family a number of years ago. He created a ritual in which he removed the sign *Daddy's Garage* that he had made for his dad prior to the divorce and abandonment. He replaced it with a sign that now read *Jason's Garage*, signifying that he no longer needed his dad's approval. Finally, there can be *rituals of continuity* that simply affirm a continuing connection. Such a ritual can be as simple as lighting a candle on the anniversary of a death, something that Rosa and her adoptive parents did on each anniversary of Maria's death.

In designing therapeutic rituals, the narrative of the loss will suggest what type of ritual will be helpful as well as who should participate. Rituals should include objects that are symbolically significant and allow the ritual focus. Other symbolic elements representing fire (candles), wind (music), water, and earth (flowers), can also be helpful. Finally, rituals need to be both planned and processed.

Rituals reach back to the beginning of human existence. Evidence of rituals offers powerful testimony that the ancients buried their dead with varied public and private ceremonial acts, long before they could write about it. Sometimes, even in therapy, we can reach back to ancient wisdom.

Kenneth J. Doka, PhD, MDiv, is a professor of gerontology at the Graduate School of The College of New Rochelle and senior consultant to Hospice Foundation of America. Dr. Doka serves as editor of HFA's Living with Grief® book series, its Journeys newsletter, and numerous other books and publications. Dr. Doka has served as a panelist on HFA's Living with Grief® video programs for 22 years. He is a past president of the Association for Death Education and Counseling (ADEC) and received the Special Contributions Award in the field of Death Education from the Association for Death Education and Counseling. He is a member and past chair of the International Work Group on Death, Dying and Bereavement. In 2006, Dr. Doka was grandfathered in as a mental health counselor under New York's first state licensure of counselors. Dr. Doka is an ordained Lutheran minister.

REFERENCES

Bolton, C. & Camp, D. (1987). Funeral rituals and the facilitation of grief work. *Omega: The Journal of Death and Dying, 17,* 343-351.

Bolton, C. & Camp, D. (1989). The post-funeral ritual in bereavement counseling and grief work. *Journal of Gerontological Social Work, 13,* 49-59.

Doka, K. (1984). Expectation of death, participation in funeral rituals, and grief adjustment. *Omega: The Journal of Death and Dying, 15,* 119-130.

Doka, K. J. (2008). The power of ritual: A gift for children and adolescents. In K. J. Doka & A. S. Tucci (Eds.), *Living with grief: Children and adolescents* (pp. 287-295). Washington, DC: Hospice Foundation of America.

Doka, K. J. & Martin, T. (2010). *Grieving beyond gender: Understanding the ways men and women grieve* (revised ed.). New York, NY: Routledge.

Gennep, A. (1960). *The rites of passage.* Chicago, IL: The University of Chicago Press.

Gross, R. & Klass, D. (1997). Tibetan Buddhism and the resolution of grief: The Bardo-Thodell for the living and the grieving. *Death Studies, 21,* 377-398.

Rando, T. A. (1984). *Grief, dying, and death: Clinical interventions for caregivers.* Champaign, IL: Research Press.

Rando, T. A. (1993). *Treatment of complicated mourning.* Champaign, IL: Research Press.

Reeves, N., & Boersma, F. (1990). The therapeutic use of ritual in maladaptive grieving. *Omega: The Journal of Death and Dying, 20,* 281-291.

Worden, J. W. (2009). *Grief counseling and therapy: A handbook for the mental health practitioner* (4th ed.). New York, NY: Springer.

CHAPTER 18

Complicated Grief Treatment

M. Katherine Shear, Natalia A. Skritskaya, and Colleen Gribbin

CASE DESCRIPTION

Helena is a 45-year-old mother whose 5-year-old son Daniel died unexpectedly six years ago. She saw a newspaper article about complicated grief (CG) and recognized herself. She knew she had to get help, mainly because her other children needed her.

Helena's childhood was difficult. She did not have a close relationship with her parents and struggled with depression throughout adolescence. She met her husband when they were both teenagers and decided to marry him because she wanted children, even though she knew he was a drinker and they fought about this and other issues. Helena has two living children, but Daniel was her favorite. He died after he developed a sore throat that persisted despite a course of antibiotics. Helena had taken him to the hospital, where his heart unexpectedly stopped; they were not able to revive him. She still feels dazed when she thinks about this. She never got a clear explanation about the cause of Daniel's death and she can't stop thinking that if she had insisted on staying with him while the doctors examined him he would not have died. She also thinks that the doctors did not try hard enough to revive him. Her only way of coping is to avoid anything that reminds her of Daniel.

STATEMENT OF PROBLEM

Helena is suffering from complicated grief (CG). Although Daniel died six years ago, she feels like she just lost him. She knows the facts but has not been able to accept what happened. She has recurring thoughts that the doctors should have done more and that she should have done something to prevent this death; as she states, "Little boys don't just die like that." She is not able to go through Daniel's things or even go into his room. She sometimes has to drive as much as an hour out of her way to avoid the hospital where he died. Helena forces herself to do what is necessary to take care of her family, but inside she is still in a lot of pain. She thinks her life is over and wishes she had died along with Daniel; she is just going through the motions of living.

ANALYSIS

Adaptation is very challenging for anyone following the sudden, unexpected death of a child. However, Helena's process of adjustment is stalled. She still exhibits frequent intense longing and yearning for her son that interferes with relationships with her children and other people and keeps her imprisoned in a futile existence. She ruminates about how Daniel did not have to die, blaming herself, the doctors, and sometimes railing against God.

Helena has a history of depression and her friends have always said she is a worrier. Her alcoholic father used to beat her if she got in his way when he was drunk. She was date-raped in high school and never told anyone. She was an average student because she often couldn't concentrate in school, although she scored very high on standardized tests. She has a good support system of family and friends though they are mostly avoiding her now. She feels they are fed up with her; they often tell her she needs to put Daniel's death behind her.

Helena scored 43 on the 19-item Inventory of Complicated Grief (ICG), well above the threshold of 30 used to identify CG. She endorsed a score of 28 on the Grief-Related Avoidance Questionnaire (GRAQ), a moderately high level of avoidance, and a score of 56 (also a high score) on the Typical Beliefs Questionnaire (TBQ) that rates problematic grief-related thoughts and beliefs. The GRAQ and TBQ are self-report questionnaires designed to measure avoidance behaviors and common maladaptive cognitions in individuals with complicated grief. The GRAQ instructs individuals to rate frequency of avoiding a number of loss-related situations. The TBQ rates statements like "You should have done something to prevent the death or make it easier," and "Life is unbearable without [the loved one who died]."

Goals of Counseling

The goal of complicated grief treatment (CGT) is to resolve grief complications and reinvigorate the natural adaptive process that entails accepting the finality and consequences of the loss, reconfiguring the relationship to the deceased (continuing bonds) and redefining life goals and plans to find a new normal. Complicated grief treatment consists of 16 sessions that incorporate both loss-related and restoration-related procedures. Core components include providing information about love, loss and grief, promoting effective self-regulation, rebuilding social connections, work on personal aspirational goals, revisiting the story of the death, revisiting the world, and work with memories.

Intervention Strategy

In the first session, Helena talked about Daniel and told the therapist how he died. They discussed what things have been like for her since then. Helena began using a daily diary to monitor high and low levels of grief intensity. She was diligent about this and noticed that some of her reactions surprised her. For example, she had not realized that there were times during the day when her grief levels were very low. She also noticed that her grief was spiking in the late afternoon every day. This was their time alone when she and Daniel would cuddle and read a book together. In the second session, the therapist asked that if she could wave a magic wand and have her grief at a manageable level, what would she want for herself. Helena was taken aback by this question. Eventually, she said maybe she would want to start working full time.

The therapist invited Helena to bring someone to the third session. She decided to invite Annette, a close friend; they had helped each other in times of need but lately talked infrequently. Annette seemed frustrated that all Helena wanted to talk about was Daniel, but when Annette mentioned him, Helena burst into tears. Annette was happy that Helena sought help and interested that the approach seemed much more structured than other therapies Helena had tried.

In the fourth session, Helena was asked to revisit the story of Daniel's death. She was apprehensive, but agreed to do it. She was asked to close her eyes, visualize herself at the hospital as the nurse tells her that Daniel has died, and tell the story of what happened from that point forward. Helena was asked to rate her distress level on a scale of 0-10 before she started and continue to do so every two minutes as she tells the story. After 10 minutes, she was asked to open her eyes and reflect on this story. The exercise was audio-recorded and she was asked to listen to it at home. Then the therapist asked her to set the story aside and plan a rewarding activity afterwards to balance the pain she has experienced.

In the fifth session, the therapist added situational revisiting, a procedure similar to in-vivo exposure used to treat phobias, in which the bereaved person develops a ranking of situations that trigger yearning and sadness and then makes a plan to revisit these situations in a systematic way. Together they developed a hierarchy of situations Helena was avoiding and made plans as to how she can confront them. The goal was to help her continue to process the loss and free her to do things in a more comfortable way.

The first imaginal revisiting exercise was short and very emotional; as the exercise was repeated over four more sessions the story grew longer and more detailed. As she reflected on the story, Helena grappled with her anger at the doctors, yet gradually came to the conclusion that they really did all they could. She also was plagued by guilt about not spending more time with Daniel during the days when he was sick, but through the exercise came to see that she could not have known that Daniel would die. She began to say that she knows she was a good mother. At a later session, Helena said that she hated listening to the tapes, but had begun to sense progress. For instance, she recently surprised herself and Annette when she had a conversation about Daniel without crying.

Helena had lost faith in God when Daniel died and had stopped going to church. As her guilt and anger receded she decided to start going to services. Her pastor was happy to see her and she found that her spirituality again provided her with comfort. Thinking that Daniel is in heaven gave her considerable relief, and she began thinking about living more fully and making good use of her life.

One of the most difficult places for Helena to confront was the hospital where Daniel died and where there were still personal items that she needed to pick up. The nurse administrator had kindly agreed to hold them for her but had started calling more frequently, saying she did not know how much longer she could keep Daniel's things. Because this place represented so many challenges, the therapist helped her break it down to more manageable steps. She began by driving past the hospital, just looking at it from a distance. After doing this every day for a week, she drove to the hospital parking lot and sat there for 10 minutes each day. From there, she walked to the door of the hospital, then to the door of the emergency room, and eventually, she was able to go into the hospital. Going through this process at the hospital also helped Helena at home. She was able to go into Daniel's room, eventually sorting his things, deciding what to keep and what to dispose of, as well as planning how she and the family could begin to use this room.

In the sixth session, Helena and her therapist started working with memories. Helena brought an album with pictures; she had many fond memories and shared them eagerly. She was also asked to think about her least favorite memories. She did not enjoy this as much, but talked about ways Daniel was difficult, as any child would be. Through these exercises she felt a strengthened connection with Daniel. In a later session, the therapist invited Helena to have an imaginal conversation with Daniel in which she first could tell him anything she wished and then take his role and answer. This exercise was a very powerful experience; afterward, Helena said she felt closer to Daniel than any time since he died.

By the end of just 16 sessions Helena felt like a new person, lighter than she had felt in six years. She is socializing again and her friends and family are very relieved. She still misses Daniel enormously and reminders of him still make her cry, but no longer send her into a day-long period of withdrawal. She is interviewing for jobs and is debating whether to go back to school. She has a sense of purpose that she may never have had before, and hope for some happiness for the first time in years.

CONCLUSIONS AND REFLECTIONS

Helena's story illustrates how a focused short-term intervention can be very helpful for someone with complicated grief. The treatment included information about attachment, loss and grief, fostering self-regulation, working on aspirational goals, building support, telling the story of the death, revisiting a world changed by loss, and building a sense of continuing bonds. As she worked through this program, Helena's anger and guilt subsided and she became freer to move about in the world, less avoidant of situational reminders and more engaged in goals and plans that felt meaningful and held some possibility for happiness. As she reflected on her experience with CGT,

Helena said she was amazed at how much better she was feeling in so short a time. She thanked the therapist and said, "You gave me my life back – and more."

M. Katherine Shear, MD, *is the Marion E. Kenworthy Professor of Psychiatry and director of the Center for Complicated Grief at Columbia School of Social Work. Dr. Shear developed complicated grief treatment and confirmed its efficacy in three large National Institute of Mental Health (NIMH)-funded studies. She is widely recognized for her work in bereavement, including both research and clinical awards from the Association for Death Education and Counseling and invited authorship of articles for* UpToDate *and* The New England Journal of Medicine.

Natalia A. Skritskaya, PhD, *is a licensed clinical psychologist, associate research scientist at Columbia School of Social Work, and a CBT therapist. She is a CGT-trained therapist and supervisor and is clinical training director at the Center for Complicated Grief. Dr. Skritskaya is interested in psychotherapy research, evidence-based mental health treatments and treatment dissemination.*

Colleen Gribbin *received a BS from Brown University and an MA in Clinical Psychology from Teachers College, Columbia University. Colleen is the program manager for the Center for Complicated Grief. She is a trained evaluator and member of the Center's assessment team, which provides guidance to professionals in evaluating people with CG.*

Index

Popular books available *now* from Hospice Foundation of America

Titles include:

The Longest Loss: Alzheimer's Disease and Dementia

Living With Grief: Helping Adolescents Cope with Loss

Improving Care for Veterans Facing Illness and Death

End-of-Life Ethics: A Case Study Approach

Beyond Kübler-Ross: New Perspectives on Death, Dying and Grief

Journeys With Grief, A Collection of Articles about Love, Life and Loss

HOSPICE FOUNDATION
OF AMERICA

www.hospicefoundation.org

(202) 457-5811 phone
(202) 457-5815 fax

The mission of Hospice Foundation of America is to provide leader-ship in the development and application of hospice and its philosophy of care with the goal of enhancing the U.S. health care system and the role of hospice within it.

NOTES

NOTES